AS Music
Literacy Workbook

Rebecca Berkley
with Paul Terry

R·

Rhinegold Education

241 Shaftesbury Avenue
London WC2H 8TF
Telephone: 020 7333 1720

LCH MUS
6/2/15 LV
£19.95

Music Study Guides

(series editor: Paul Terry)

GCSE, AS and A2 Music Study Guides (AQA, Edexcel and OCR)

GCSE, AS and A2 Music Listening Tests (AQA, Edexcel and OCR)

GCSE Music Study Guide (WJEC)

AS/A2 Music Technology Study Guide (Edexcel)

AS/A2 Music Technology Listening Tests (Edexcel)

Lifelines Revision Guides for GCSE (AQA, Edxcel and OCR), AS and A2 Music (AQA and Edexcel)

Lifelines Revision Guides AS and A2 Music Technology (Edexcel)

Also available from Rhinegold Education

Key Stage 3 Elements

Key Stage 3 Listening Tests: Book 1 and Book 2

GCSE and AS Music Composition and Literacy Workbooks

AS and A2 Music Harmony Workbooks

Baroque Music in Focus, Romanticism in Focus, Modernism in Focus

Batman in Focus, *Goldfinger* in Focus, *Immaculate Collection* in Focus, *Who's Next* in Focus

Film Music in Focus, Musicals in Focus

Rhinegold also publishes Classical Music, Classroom Music, Early Music Today, Music Teacher,
Opera Now, Piano, The Singer, Teaching Drama, British and International Music Yearbook,
British Performing Arts Yearbook, British Music Education Yearbook, Rhinegold Dictionary of Music in Sound.

First published 2009 in Great Britain by
Rhinegold Publishing Limited
239–241 Shaftesbury Avenue
London WC2H 8TF
Telephone: 020 7333 1720
Fax: 020 7333 1765
www.rhinegold.co.uk
© Rhinegold Publishing Limited 2009

Rhinegold Publishing Ltd has used its best efforts in preparing this workbook. It does not assume,
and hereby disclaims any liability to any party, for loss or damage caused by errors or omissions in the book,
whether such errors or omissions result from negligence, accident or other cause.

If you are preparing for an exam in music you should always check the current requirements of the
examination, since these may change from one year to the next.

AS Music Literacy Workbook

British Library Cataloguing in Publication Data.
A catalogue record for this book is available from the British Library.
ISBN 978-1-906178-46-8
Printed in Great Britain by Headley Brothers Ltd

Contents

Authors

Rebecca Berkley

Rebecca is a freelance writer and musician. She is currently the SingUp Area Leader for West Berkshire, and works as a choral conductor. She is the co-author of Rhinegold's *Edexcel GCSE Music Listening Tests (Book 3)* and *GCSE Music Literacy Workbook*. She also contributes as a freelance writer to *Classroom Music* Magazine.

Paul Terry

Paul Terry has taught music from primary to postgraduate level. He was a music examiner for nearly 30 years and has been engaged as a consultant by several examination boards. He also served as a member of the Secondary Examinations Council and its successor the Schools Examinations and Assessment Council. He was chief examiner for the Oxford and Cambridge Schools Examinations Board (now part of OCR) and a chief examiner for London Examinations (now part of Edexcel). In addition to the books he has written for Rhinegold Publishing, Paul is co-author with William Lloyd of *Music in Sequence*, *Classics in Sequence*, *Rock in Sequence*, and *Rehearse, Direct and Play*, published by Musonix Publishing. He is also co-author with David Bowman of *Aural Matters*, *Aural Matters in Practice* and *Listening Matters*, published by Schott.

Acknowledgements

The authors would like to thank Lucien Jenkins for his editorial suggestions and guidance, and Harriet Power, Katherine Smith, Matthew Hammond and Adrian Horsewood at Rhinegold Publishing for their assistance in the editorial and production process.

Introduction

This book builds on the work of the *GCSE Music Literacy Workbook*. It will help you learn how to read and understand notation at a level suitable for AS music. Throughout the book, there are exercises to complete which will lead you step by step through the new information you have learnt. There are also a number of longer revision exercises in the final chapter.

If you are starting on AS music, you probably already understand some notation, and so are used to reading musical notes and symbols. You will probably be quite fluent in reading music for the instruments you play, and may be able to read other types of notation, such as the treble and bass clef in music written for piano or keyboard. This book introduces and explains a wide range of different types of notation used in music of the last 400 years, including rock, pop and jazz. We explore the subject in more detail than in the *GCSE Music Literacy Workbook*, and discuss more complex concepts such as tonality.

What's in the book?

The book opens with a chapter on rhythm. We investigate the nuts and bolts of rhythm notation including rests, dotted notes, triplets and tuplets, and consider a wide range of different time signatures and how these interact with pulse and tempo. We discuss special rhythmic effects like syncopation and swung quavers, and how these are notated.

The next chapter deals with different scales. It opens with a brief revision of major and minor scales, and explores how major and minor keys are related. We discuss the concept of tonality in music. The chapter also investigates intervals and different types of scales and modes, including the blues scale and whole-tone scale.

Chapter 3 is concerned with reading harmony. We discuss ways to label chords with Roman numerals (commonly used in classical music) and chord symbols (which are more widely used in jazz, rock and pop). We describe ways to identify and read specific chords, such as the dominant seventh, secondary dominants and chromatic chords; harmonic devices like non-chord notes; and modulations.

Chapter 4 focuses on ways to notate special performance techniques. We start with articulation marks and then discuss special notation for particular instruments such as percussion, strings, piano, and writing tablature for guitar and bass guitar. The chapter ends with a review of symbols used for ornaments.

Chapter 5 investigates score reading. It opens with a discussion of clefs, and then moves onto detailed examination of how to read scores for up to three instruments, vocal scores, scores for larger ensembles, lead sheets and jazz and pop arrangements. We also look at writing and reading music for transposing instruments.

Chapter 6 includes a number of revision exercises, with questions that bring together all of the knowledge learnt in the rest of the book. The answers to these exercises can be found on the Rhinegold website (www.rhinegold.co.uk). They are available to download as a PDF from the relevant webpage for the *AS Music Literacy Workbook*.

1. Rhythm

Note durations and time signatures

Notes and rests

Here are the standard symbols for note lengths and rests. Rests are normally drawn in *exactly* the vertical positions shown on the staves below:

Name of note or rest	Breve	Semibreve	Minim	Crotchet	Quaver	Semiquaver	Demisemi-quaver
American name	Double whole note	Whole note	Half note	Quarter note	Eighth note	Sixteenth note	Thirty second note
Number of units	8	4	2	1	$\frac{1}{2}$	$\frac{1}{4}$	$\frac{1}{8}$
What the note looks like	⫿𝅃⫿ or ⫿𝅃⫿ or ⫿⫿	𝅝	𝅗𝅥	𝅘𝅥	𝅘𝅥𝅮	𝅘𝅥𝅯	𝅘𝅥𝅰
What the rest looks like	𝄺	𝄻	𝄼	𝄽	𝄾	𝄿	𝅀

For more information on the basics of reading and writing rhythms, see the first three chapters of the *GCSE Music Literacy Workbook*.

A semibreve rest is used to indicate a whole bar's rest in any time except $\frac{4}{2}$ (in which a breve rest is used). Whole-bar rests are always positioned in the centre of the bar, rather than on the first beat:

Multi-bar rests are often used in parts for individual instruments in order to save space and to make the music easier to follow. In the example below, the bass player has eight bars of rests before rehearsal letter A, and then another four bars of rests before starting to play. Splitting the 12 bars of rests in this way allows the musician to follow the part if a rehearsal needs to re-start at letter A:

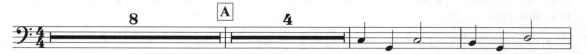

Dotted notes and dotted rests

Adding a dot after a note or rest increases its length by half. For example, where a minim lasts for two units, a dotted minim lasts for three. The dot is drawn to the right of the note or rest, and is centred in a space between the stave lines:

Name of note or rest	Dotted breve	Dotted semibreve	Dotted minim	Dotted crotchet	Dotted quaver	Dotted semiquaver	Dotted demisemi-quaver
Number of units	12	6	3	$1\frac{1}{2}$	$\frac{3}{4}$	$\frac{3}{8}$	$\frac{3}{16}$
What the notes looks like	⫿𝅃⫿·	𝅝·	𝅗𝅥·	𝅘𝅥·	𝅘𝅥𝅮·	𝅘𝅥𝅯·	𝅘𝅥𝅰·
What the rest looks like	𝄺·	𝄻·	𝄼·	𝄽·	𝄾·	𝄿·	𝅀·

Dotted rests are not used in simple time unless they are less than a crotchet in length, but they are frequently used in compound time.

Time signatures

The upper figure in a time signature tells us how many beats there are in each bar, and the lower figure indicates the type of beat being used. For example, $\frac{4}{4}$ means that there are four crotchet beats in a bar, while $\frac{3}{8}$ tells us that there are three quaver beats in a bar.

- ➤ In **simple time**, the upper figure is usually 2, 3 or 4 and each beat can be divided into **two** equal parts. For example, $\frac{3}{4}$ indicates that there are three crotchet beats in each bar, each of which can be divided into two quavers.

- ➤ In **compound time**, the upper figure is usually 6, 9 or 12 and each beat can be divided into **three** equal parts (so one beat is formed from three of the units indicated by the lower figure in the time signature). For example, $\frac{6}{8}$ means that there are six quavers in each bar, normally grouped into two beats of three quavers each.

We can see the difference between simple and compound time by comparing the two rhythms in the example below. Each rhythm has six quavers in the first bar, but because they have different time signatures the quavers are grouped differently, which affects both how they look and how they sound.

- ➤ $\frac{3}{4}$ is a simple time, so the quavers are grouped in pairs, forming three beats

- ➤ $\frac{6}{8}$ is a compound time, so the quavers are grouped in threes, forming two beats.

This means that the quavers in the first rhythm are beamed in crotchet beats, but the quavers in the second rhythm are beamed in dotted-crotchet beats. In the first rhythm, you would emphasise the first, third and fifth quavers as you clapped it out loud, and in the second rhythm you would emphasise the first and fourth quavers.

Say the words aloud as you clap these rhythms:

Did you pass your test to - day?

Text me as soon as you can.

The following table gives the most commonly used time signatures:

	Simple time	Compound time
Duple (two beats per bar)	$\frac{2}{2}$ $\frac{2}{4}$ $\frac{2}{8}$	$\frac{6}{4}$ $\frac{6}{8}$
Triple (three beats per bar)	$\frac{3}{2}$ $\frac{3}{4}$ $\frac{3}{8}$	$\frac{9}{4}$ $\frac{9}{8}$
Quadruple (four beats per bar)	$\frac{4}{2}$ $\frac{4}{4}$ $\frac{4}{8}$	$\frac{12}{4}$ $\frac{12}{8}$

The symbol **C** (often called 'common time') means the same as $\frac{4}{4}$, while **¢** (often referred to as 'cut-C' time) is the same as $\frac{2}{2}$.

A time signature is normally written before the first note of a piece, and at the start of any bar where the time changes. It is not written at the start of every stave.

If a change of time occurs at the start of a stave, the new time signature is often *also* written at the end of the previous stave, after the last barline, as an early warning.

Grouping notes and rests

Beaming notes

To make rhythms easier to read, short notes (anything less than a crotchet) are joined together by beams wherever possible. These replace the flags on separate notes, like this:

As a general rule, notes are beamed in one-beat groups according to the time signature. In the example above, the beams allow us to see that there are four beats in the bar rather than just a jumble of short notes.

In 6/8 the beat is a dotted crotchet, and so short notes are beamed in dotted-crotchet groups in order to make the main beats clear:

Beams that are attached to a note at only one end always point inwards to make the beat clear, so we write:

not:

Beams can also straddle a rest between notes, providing they don't extend beyond the beat concerned:

Beams do not normally extend beyond a single beat except in the following cases:

➢ Four quavers may be beamed together to form a complete bar in 2/4 time, or to form the first or second half of a bar in 4/4 time (but they are never used across the middle of a 4/4 bar):

➢ Six quavers may be beamed together to form a complete bar in 3/4 time, but this is never done in 6/8 time:

Occasionally, rhythms are beamed in other ways (even across barlines), usually to emphasise how the notes should be phrased, but in most cases it is best to keep to the principles outlined above.

Exercise 1

Add the correct time signature to the start of each of the following melodies, which all begin on the first beat of a bar. Remember to look at the grouping and beaming of the notes, as well as counting the number of beats in each bar.

1.

Trad: *Golden Slumbers* (17th-century lullaby)

Andante

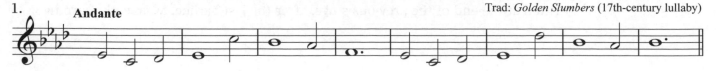

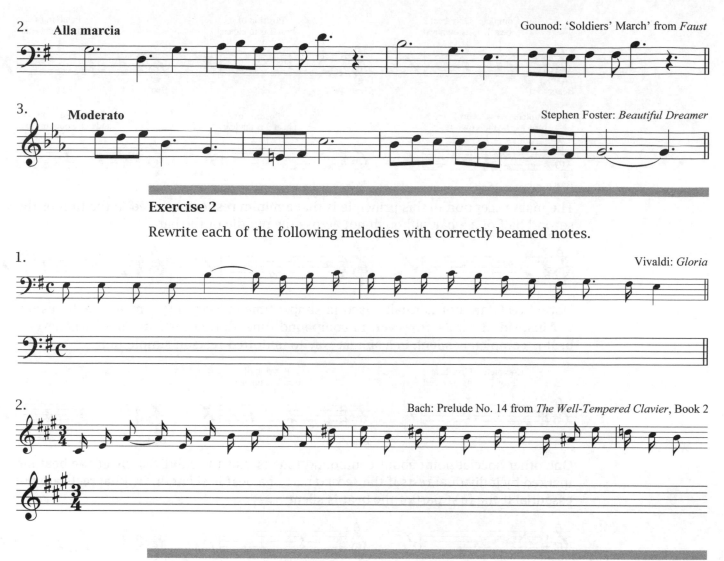

2. **Alla marcia**

Gounod: 'Soldiers' March' from *Faust*

3. **Moderato**

Stephen Foster: *Beautiful Dreamer*

Exercise 2

Rewrite each of the following melodies with correctly beamed notes.

1.

Vivaldi: *Gloria*

2.

Bach: Prelude No. 14 from *The Well-Tempered Clavier*, Book 2

Exercise 3

The following melody has been wrongly beamed. Rewrite it with correct beaming for $\frac{6}{8}$. Notice that it does not start on the first beat of a bar.

Sullivan: *The Mikado*

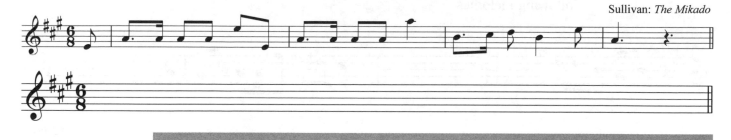

Grouping rests

Rests can't be beamed like notes, but they should be written to make the position of the main beats as clear as possible. Although we shall meet several exceptions shortly, the general rule is to add one or more rests to fill any beat that is incomplete, and then to write a single rest on each remaining beat. Study the following examples carefully – every bar adds up to the correct number of beats, but only the first bar in each row is written clearly and correctly:

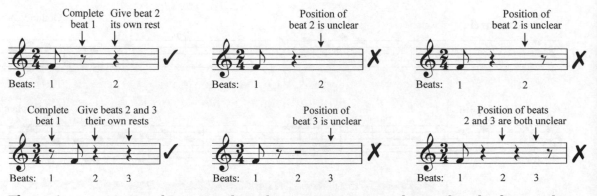

The main exception to this principle is that a minim rest can be used in the first or the second half of a $\frac{4}{4}$ bar, although not across the middle of the bar:

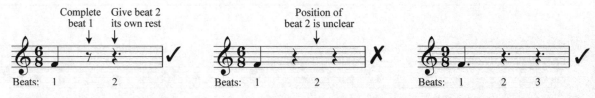

Dotted rests are not normally used in simple time (although you may sometimes see ⁊· ♪ instead of ⁊ ⁊ ♪). However, in compound time, dotted rests are used whenever a beat is completely silent, in a similar way to undotted rests in simple time:

One other special point about compound time is that the subdivisions of the beat are marked by individual rests if the *second* part of a beat is silent. Individual rests are not essential if the first part of the beat is silent:

Exercise 4

Add the correct rest(s) to complete the bar at each of the places marked ✱ in the following melodies.

Tempo and time signature

A metronome is a device that produces a regular number of clicks per minute, used to indicate the tempo of a piece. A metronome marking tells us how fast to play a piece by specifying how many beats per minute there should be.

The vast majority of western music has a clearly identifiable beat. It is what we tap our foot to when we listen to the music, and is sometimes called the pulse. The speed of the beat is referred to as the tempo of the music. Music can be performed at a variety of tempi, and the tempo can change during the course of a piece. Since the early 19th century, many composers have used metronome markings to indicate tempo: for example, ♩ = 120 means that there are 120 crotchet beats per minute, or two a second – quite a fast tempo. In pop music scores, the same tempo is often shown as 120bpm, where bpm means beats per minute.

Tempo and time signature work together when we read or write music. For example, although the two following excerpts look different, they sound exactly the same. In the first the beat is a crotchet while in the second it is a minim, but the tempo marking indicates that the speed of the beat (120 beats per minute) is the same in both:

Try playing *Dance ti thy Daddy* at a much faster speed and tap your foot to the beat. You may find that tapping three beats per bar is too fast to be comfortable and that it is more natural to tap only on the first beat of each bar.

The pulse we feel is dependent on the tempo of the music. If the speed is fast, we may feel fewer beats than the time signature suggests. Conversely, if the tempo is very slow we may find ourselves tapping more frequently than the time signature suggests – for instance, eight quavers a bar in a very slow 4/4 time.

Other note lengths

Triplets

We can create triplets with various note durations. In each case, the three notes in the triplet will equal the length of two of the same notes. Notes in a triplet are beamed together if they are less than a crotchet in length, and the triplet is indicated by writing the figure *3* above or below the beam. If there is no beam, or any doubt about which notes are affected, square brackets are drawn either side of the *3* to indicate the notes concerned.

A semiquaver triplet		equals two semiquavers	
A quaver triplet		equals two quavers	
A crotchet triplet		equals two crotchets	
A minim triplet		equals two minims	

Within a triplet, you can write any combination of notes or rests which add up to the appropriate duration:

If a triplet pattern continues for some bars, the triplet signs are often omitted after the first bar. The Italian word *simile* ('similar') or the abbreviation *sim.* can be used to confirm that the rhythmic pattern continues, but this is not essential.

Duplets

A triplet divides a note into three equal parts. In compound time, where the beats are normally divided into three, duplets can be used to divide a note into two equal parts. Like triplets, you can use any note duration in a duplet. The duplet is indicated by the figure *2* centred on the beam. If there is no beam, or any doubt about which notes are affected, a bracket is needed as well as the numeral.

A duplet takes the time of three of the same note:

We can create duplets using a range of different note durations:

A semiquaver duplet		equals three semiquavers		equals a dotted quaver	
A quaver duplet		equals three quavers		equals a dotted crotchet	
A crotchet duplet		equals three crotchets		equals a dotted minim	
A minim duplet		equals three minims		equals a dotted semibreve	

In compound time, dotted notes can be used to achieve the same rhythm as duplets. The two following melodies sound exactly the same:

Exercise 5

Using triplets where necessary, rewrite the following melody in $\frac{4}{4}$, keeping the rhythm the same. The first five beats have been given.

Gounod: 'Soldiers' March' from *Faust*

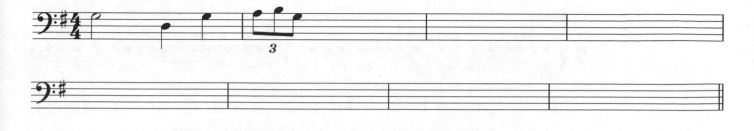

Other tuplets

Duplets and triplets are not the only non-standard rhythmic groupings. It is possible to use four notes where three are expected (a quadruplet) or five where four are expected (a quintuplet) and so on. These are often known collectively as tuplets. Here a semiquaver quintuplet is written in the space of four regular semiquavers in bar 1, and a quaver septuplet is written in the space of four regular quavers in bar 3:

To read these rhythms accurately, try fitting them to words or phrases such as un-con-ven-tion-al (five syllables) or hea-vy hip-po-pot-a-mus (seven syllables).

Double-dotted notes and rests

We learnt earlier that adding a dot to a note increases its length by half. Adding two dots, or double dotting the note, increases its value by a further quarter of the original note value. For example, a minim is worth two beats, a dotted minim is worth three beats, and a double-dotted minim is worth 3½ beats:

> Some types of baroque music are, by convention, performed with double-dotted rhythms even though they are notated with single dotted notes.

Rests can be double dotted in the same way as notes. Triple dotting, although rare, is also possible. Double- and triple-dotted notes are usually followed by a short note to round-up the number of beats to a whole number, as in this example below:

Verdi: *Requiem*

Rex tre - men - dae ma - je - sta - tis!

Exercise 6

The following melody begins on the first beat of a bar. Write the correct time signature at the start and add the correct rest(s) to complete the bar at each of the places marked ✳.

Irregular time signatures

Irregular time signatures, such as $\frac{5}{4}$, often consist of the alternation of familiar patterns of beats such as three and two. We can see this in the following example, where Holst's choice of notes (dotted minims alternating with ordinary minims) clarifies the division of $\frac{5}{4}$ into patterns of 3+2 beats:

Allegro   Holst: 'Mars' from *The Planets*

A similar process can be seen in the following example, where $\frac{7}{4}$ is divided into patterns of 4+3 beats:

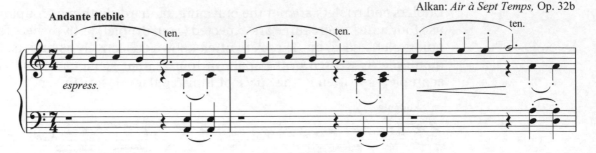

Alkan: *Air à Sept Temps,* Op. 32b

More complex patterns of beats can be indicated by composite time signatures. In the example below, the time signature indicates that eight quavers per bar are to be articulated in the pattern 3+2+3 (compare this with the eight quavers in the $\frac{4}{4}$ bar that follows):

In this example the time signature indicates that the music has alternate bars of $\frac{6}{8}$ and $\frac{3}{4}$ (a rhythm that features prominently in the song 'America' from Bernstein's *West Side Story*):

Exercise 7

Each of the following melodies starts on the first beat of the bar and contains several changes of time signature. Add the correct time signature at each place marked ✽. Remember to look at the beaming of the notes as well as counting the length of each bar in order to work out the time signature.

Remember to add a cautionary time signature for the beginning of the next line

Rhythmic effects

Syncopation

Syncopation temporarily alters the normal accent pattern of a time signature. It is created by emphasising a weak beat, or a note between beats – often by having a rest or a tied note where a strong beat is expected. Much Latin-American dance music is built on repetitions of the following syncopated pattern, known as *son clave*:

In bar 1, there is no note on the third beat – instead, the second note of the pattern falls between beats two and three – and in bar 2 there is no note at all on the strong first beat of the bar.

A syncopated rhythm is often made more obvious by combining it with rhythms which play on the beat, as in the following example:

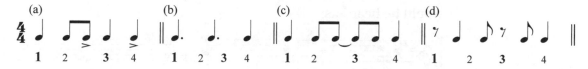

Syncopation can be shown in the following ways:

> With accents, as in (a) below

> By using a dotted note or tie, so that a new note doesn't sound on the next strong beat, as in (b) and (c)

> By placing rests on strong beats, as in (d).

It is common practice to use a minimal number of ties when writing syncopated rhythms, especially in modern percussion music, jazz and Latin-American music.

Swing rhythms

In jazz and the blues, pairs of quavers are often played with a lean on the first note, making it longer than the second. Listen to Duke Ellington's *Take the 'A' Train*, or *It Don't Mean a Thing (If It Ain't Got That Swing)* or any other up-tempo number by Count Basie, Benny Goodman, Artie Shaw or Glenn Miller, and you are likely to hear the drummer playing a swing rhythm. This can't be notated precisely, as the relative lengths of the two notes can vary according to the speed and style of the music, but any of the following approximations can be used:

The first of these is the simplest method, as the others can result in very complex notation if syncopation also occurs (as it frequently does in jazz and the blues), but it is important to include the instruction 'swing' and/or the direction ♪♪ = ♪♪ at the start of the music.

If normal quavers are required in music where the rhythm is otherwise swung, add the instruction 'straight 8s' (meaning even-length quavers).

Cross-rhythm, hemiola and polyrhythm

A **cross-rhythm** occurs when a rhythm cuts across the regular pattern of beats suggested by the time signature. In the following example, repeated groups of three quavers take the place of the pairs of quavers that we would normally expect in a simple time such as $\frac{3}{4}$:

Grieg: 'Waltz' from *Lyric Pieces*, Op. 38 No. 15

A similar type of cross-rhythm is common in ragtime, where it is known as 'secondary rag'. Here four groups of three semiquavers (marked by brackets) occupy the space of three groups of four semiquavers (shown by the beaming):

A **hemiola** is a cross-rhythm in which two groups of three beats are played to sound like three groups of two. Although found in music of all periods, it is a device often heard at triple-time cadences in Baroque music. These three bars:

Corelli: Concerto Grosso, Op. 6 No. 8

would be heard as:

Cross-rhythms can also occur between simultaneous lines in a piece. In bar 1 of the next example, the normal quavers in the melody conflict with triplet quavers in the middle parts, while in bar 2 a crotchet triplet in the melody also conflicts with normal crotchets in the bass:

Debussy: String Quartet, Op. 10

If conflicting rhythms are used throughout an extended passage, the music can be described as **polyrhythmic**. The following excerpt comes from a polyrhythmic piece in which the right hand has triplet quavers throughout while the left hand uses normal quaver rhythms:

Polyrhythms are often heard in Cuban rumba, Indian Carnatic music, West African drumming and minimalist music.

Exercise 8

Draw a bracket over *two* pairs of bars that form a hemiola in this melody.

Augmentation and diminution

A rhythm is augmented when all of its note lengths are doubled. In the following example, the theme in the top part is accompanied by an augmented version of the same theme in the bass:

A rhythm is diminished when all of its note lengths are halved. In the next example, the opening theme is imitated in diminution an octave higher by the top part, starting halfway through bar 3:

Interruptions to the pulse

Although the speed of the beat may vary, it is normally continuous throughout a piece or an individual movement. If a brief interruption to the pulse is required, it is usually indicated by a pause sign (◠), also known as a fermata. The symbol is usually written above a note or a rest, but it can also be written below for clarity (as in the next example). Its precise length is left to the discretion of the performer(s), although the Italian word *longa* ('long') or *poco* ('little') can be added if required.

If there is more than one line in the music, it is important that a clearly positioned fermata appears in all of the parts, even if they are resting. In the following example, (a) is not totally clear because the pause could apply to the quaver rest. By splitting the semibreve into two minims, the notation in (b) removes this doubt:

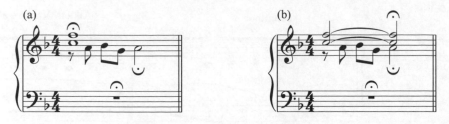

A fermata is sometimes placed over the final double bar of a movement, in which case it indicates that there should be a pause before starting the next movement.

The letters G.P. above a rest, whether or not accompanied by a fermata, stand for 'general pause' and are used to indicate that *everyone* is silent at that point. G.P is generally used only when the silence is unexpected.

A very short break in the pulse is sometimes marked with a sign called a caesura – two diagonal dashes written on the top line of the stave (as shown left).

The instruction *Tempo rubato* (or just *rubato*) indicates that the pulse should be flexible rather than strict. The Italian word *rubato* means 'robbed' and refers to stealing part of the length of one note to give to another. For example, one crotchet might be slightly shortened in order to give prominence to the next crotchet by making it slightly longer. Rubato is associated with slow pieces from the Romantic period but is often used, even when not marked in the score, in expressive music of all kinds, including soul, blues and slow pop ballads. Precisely how it is applied is down to the discretion and experience of the performer.

Free rhythm

Not all music has a regular beat. The following example is taken from the middle of a piece by Schumann in which the composer uses a free rhythm, without barlines, to allow the pianist to expressively reflect the work's title, *The Poet Speaks*:

Schumann: 'Der Dichter spricht' from *Kinderszenen*

Plainsong (or plainchant) is normally notated in free rhythm, usually with just note heads to show pitches, as in the example below. Here, the rhythm is dictated by the rhythm of the words rather than by a regular beat. Small tick marks on the upper line of the stave show breaks at the ends of phrases:

Music with a free rhythm can be described as *ametric* ('without metre'), and is also used in avant garde and electronic music of the late 20th century by composers such as Stockhausen (in the works *Kontakte, Prozession, Zyklus*), Cage (*Fontana Mix*), and Berio (*Sequenzas*). These composers created their own styles of graphic notation to indicate the way the rhythms could be performed.

Exercise 9

Look at the following passage and then answer the questions that follow.

Haydn: String Quartet in G, Op.33 No. 5

1. What term describes the rhythm of the topmost part in bars 1–2?

2. What does the abbreviation G.P. mean in bar 9?

3. What is the meaning of the figure 2 above the rests in bar 15?

4. Explain why the following rests are incorrect and indicate how they can be improved:

   (a) bar 10 (treble stave)

   (b) bar 14 (topmost part)

   (c) bar 14 (bass stave)

5. Rewrite the melody of bars 17–20 in augmentation. The time signature and first note are given below:

2. Scales and keys

Major scales and keys

In the *GCSE Music Literacy Workbook* we learnt that an ascending major scale has the following pattern of tones (T) and semitones (S): T–T–S–T–T–T–S. We also learnt that every letter name in the scale is only used once (so the first four notes of an A major scale are A–B–C♯–D, not A–B–D♭–D) . Here are some of the major scales we encountered in that book:

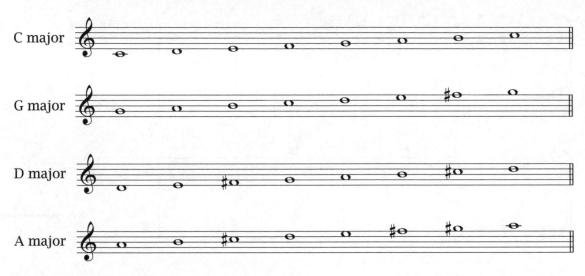

Can you see that each time the starting note goes up a 5th (or down a 4th), another sharp is needed to maintain the correct pattern of tones and semitones? Notice also that the extra sharp is added to the leading note (seventh degree) of each major scale.

Exercise 1

Following the same pattern of T–T–S–T–T–T–S, add sharps before the notes that need them to make the major scales named below.

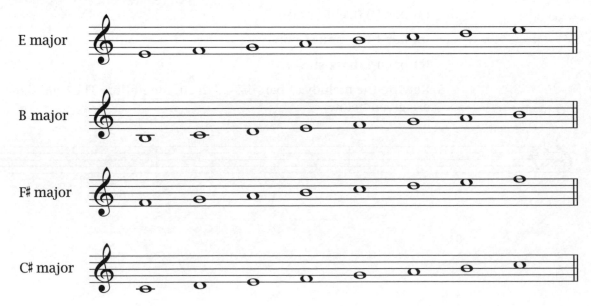

If you completed this exercise correctly, you will have found that in the key of C♯ major all seven different pitches need a sharp. Here is the complete set of sharps, in the order added, written as key signatures:

For basic information on key signatures see the *GCSE Music Literacy Workbook,* pp.43–44.

The complete order can be learnt by memorising the sentence <u>F</u>ather <u>C</u>harles <u>G</u>oes <u>D</u>own <u>A</u>nd <u>E</u>nds <u>B</u>attle. When writing key signatures with fewer sharps, always keep to this order, writing them in the positions shown above.

Now let's turn to major scales that need flats rather than sharps. Again, we'll start from C major, which needs no sharps or flats:

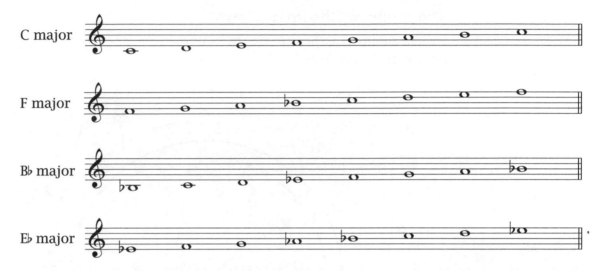

With flats, each time the starting note of the scale goes down a 5th or up a 4th (the reverse direction to sharps), another flat is needed to maintain the correct pattern of tones and semitones.

Exercise 2

Following the pattern of T–T–S–T–T–T–S, add flats before the notes that need them to make the major scales named below.

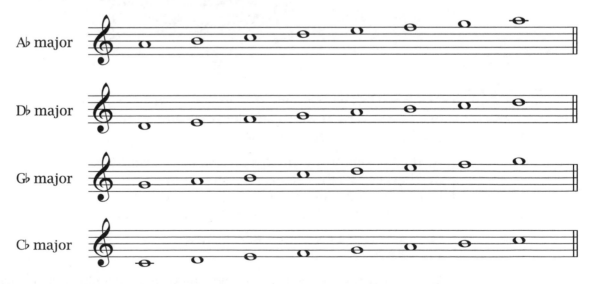

If you completed this exercise correctly, you will have found that every pitch needs a flat in the key of C♭ major. Here is the complete set of flats, in the order added, written as key signatures:

This order can be learnt by memorising the sentence <u>B</u>attle <u>E</u>nds <u>A</u>nd <u>D</u>own <u>G</u>oes <u>C</u>harles' <u>F</u>ather – which is the reverse of the order of sharps and the reason why we use this rather strange but reversible sentence to remember the order.

When writing key signatures with fewer flats, always keep to this order, writing them in the positions shown above.

The circle of 5ths (major keys)

We can summarise the key signatures of the 12 major keys by writing them in a diagram known as the circle of 5ths:

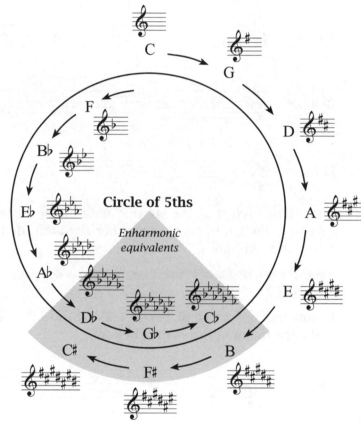

Enharmonic notes sound the same but are written differently. F is enharmonically the same as E♯, and A♭ is enharmonically the same as G♯.

As we go clockwise around the circle, each key is a 5th above the previous one and has one more sharp. If we go anticlockwise around the circle, each key is a 5th below the previous one and has one more flat.

At the bottom of the circle, the keys of G♭ major (six flats) and F♯ major (six sharps) overlap because they sound the same, even though written differently. They are said to be **enharmonic equivalents**. The keys either side are also enharmonic equivalents, but we usually choose the version with the least number of sharps or flats.

Exercise 3

Write one octave of each of the following scales in semibreves. In each case, start on the given note and don't use a key signature.

E major
going down

F♯ major going up

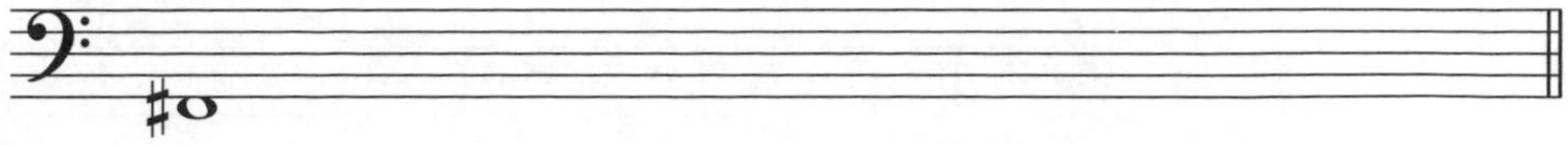

A♭ major going down

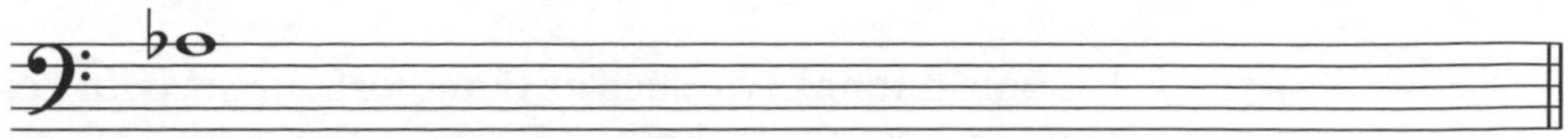

D♭ major going up

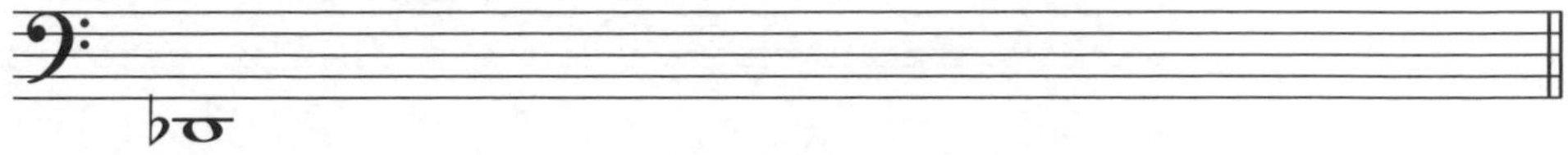

Minor scales and minor keys

Every major key has a relative minor which shares the same key signature. To find the name of the relative minor, start on note 6 of the major scale:

A♭ major

We can see from this example that the relative minor of A♭ major is F minor.

Another way to find the name of the relative minor is to count down two scale steps from the tonic of the major key. In the example above, you would start on A♭ and count two steps down the major scale, through G to F. You have then found the name of the relative minor: F minor.

If you write out the minor scale with exactly the same sharps or flats as its relative major, you will have a type of scale known as the **natural minor**. Here is one octave of F natural minor, going up and down, written with a key signature:

Usually the seventh note of a minor scale is raised by a semitone, so it leads more convincingly to the upper tonic. This scale is known as the **harmonic minor**:

The accidental that raises the seventh note has to be added whenever needed – it cannot form part of the key signature.

The reason for raising the seventh degree is so that it matches the leading note of a major scale, just a semitone below the upper tonic. The rise of a semitone from leading note to tonic gives an important sense of completion. However, it leaves an awkward gap of a tone and a half between the sixth and seventh degrees in the harmonic minor scale (D♭ to E♮ above). This is avoided in the **melodic minor** scale, in which notes 6 and 7 are both raised when going up, and are then returned to normal when going down:

A note can only be raised a semitone by a natural sign if it was flat in the first place. If the original note is already natural, it will need a sharp to raise it by a semitone and a natural sign to restore it to normal, as occurs with note 7 of G melodic minor:

In some minor keys (such as G♯ minor), the seventh degree is already sharp and therefore needs a new symbol to raise it by a semitone – the **double sharp** (x):

F𝄪 is enharmonically the same as G, but we can't use G because every letter name can only be used once in a major or minor scale, and here the letter G has already been used for the tonic (G♯).

The double sharp is matched by the double flat (♭♭), which is a whole tone below the unaltered note of the same name – for example, A♭♭ is a semitone below A♭, a tone below A, and the enharmonic equivalent of G. Double flats are not normally used in any key, but they do sometimes appear as chromatic notes outside the key.

As you can tell from their names, the harmonic minor tends to be used for chords, and the melodic minor for melodies. But there are no hard and fast rules – composers use whatever version best suits the context. You will sometimes find notes from the ascending melodic minor used when descending (as in the bass part of the example by Vivaldi on page 27), and melodies that use notes from the harmonic minor scale.

Exercise 4

Write one octave going up and going down of each of the following scales. In each case, start on the given note, use the given key signature, add all necessary accidentals and write the scale in minims.

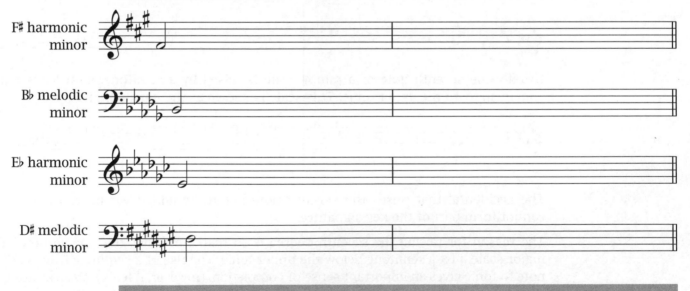

F♯ harmonic minor

B♭ melodic minor

E♭ harmonic minor

D♯ melodic minor

Speed reading key signatures

Remember these useful tips to work out a key signature quickly:

➤ C major and A minor have no sharps or flats in their key signatures

➤ The tonic of a major key with sharps is one semitone higher than the last sharp in the key signature

➤ The tonic of a major key with flats is the same as the name of the penultimate flat in the key signature, apart from F major which has only one flat

> The tonic of a minor key is one semitone above its raised seventh degree (check that your result matches the key signature, because other notes in the key could be altered by accidentals).

In the next section we will see that music can change key without changing key signature, so remember that this quick and easy method only works in simple cases.

Understanding tonality

Tonality is nothing to do with the tone colour of sounds – it is about the key(s) of the music, as defined by its cadences. To work out a key, we have to identify which scale the music is based on and check that this key is confirmed by a cadence. Look at the following passage:

Beethoven: Piano Sonata in G minor, Op. 49 No. 1

See chapters 6-7 of the *GCSE Music Literacy Workbook* for basic information on keys, cadences and modulation.

We can see from the key signature and these opening bars that all but one of the notes come from the key of G minor (E♮ and F♯ are the raised sixth and seventh degrees of that key – they form part of the ascending melodic minor scale), and the key is confirmed by an imperfect cadence in G minor at the end of the extract. As all the notes come from the key of G minor they are called **diatonic** (a term used to refer to notes from the current key), apart from the G♯ in bar 6. This note doesn't occur in G minor, and is therefore called a **chromatic** note (a term used to refer to non-diatonic notes that add colour to the music). This chromatic note doesn't affect the key – there is no cadence in any key that includes G♯ (such as A minor) in this example, so we can be sure that G♯ merely provides chromatic decoration.

In tonal music there is usually one main key in which the music begins and ends, but in between composers usually visit other keys to provide contrast. Look at this excerpt from the start of a short piano piece:

Schumann: 'Soldier's March' from *Album for the Young*

There are no accidentals in the first four-bar phrase, so we can work out the starting key from the key signature alone – it is G major, and this is confirmed by a perfect cadence in G in bar 4. In the last two bars, C♮ has been replaced by C♯. We now have two sharps, suggesting the key of D major, and this modulation (change of key) is confirmed by the perfect cadence in the last bar.

So, we now know that accidentals can have three different functions. They can be:

> The altered sixth or seventh degrees of a minor key

> Chromatic notes that are nothing to do with the key

> Notes belonging to a new key to which the music has modulated.

Remember, for accidentals to be part of a key, there needs to be a cadence (preferably perfect) to confirm that key.

Exercise 5

The following hymn consists of four phrases. Name the key in which each phrase ends.

Smallwood: *Antwerp*

The third phrase of the exercise above starts with notes from the key of A♭ major (three of this key's flats are in the key signature, and the fourth – D♭ – occurs as an accidental). There is no cadence in A♭ major because cadences come at the end of phrases. However, the V–I progression in A♭ major, marked by a bracket, gives a strong feeling of A♭ major in the middle of the phrase. In a case such as this we could say that the third phrase 'passes *through* A♭ major' on its way to the key at the end of the phrase.

Exercise 6

Look at this excerpt from a keyboard piece and identify the key of each of the four bracketed sections. Then name the only chromatic pitch in the excerpt.

Mozart: Allegro in B♭, K. 3

Try to be aware of the tonality when you are listening to music, but don't fall into the trap of thinking that major keys are always bright and happy, while minor keys are sad and mournful. The mood of a piece is determined as much by its tempo, style and instrumentation as the key used. For example, the march from Handel's oratorio *Saul*, which is often played at state funerals, is in C major, but sounds mournful because it has a very slow, solemn tread and is scored for soft, low strings, trombones and kettledrums:

On the other hand, Vivaldi's Concerto for Two Violins in A minor sounds lively and energetic, despite its minor key, because of its fast tempo, loud dynamic and bustling rhythms:

Vivaldi: Concerto for Two Violins, Op. 3 No. 8

The only sure way to tell major from minor is to listen for the third degree of the scale. If it is normally major, particularly in the tonic chord, the key is major; if it is normally minor, the key is minor. Try playing the 'Dead March' from *Saul* as written above, very slowly in C major (count eight quavers per bar). Then play it with E♭ and A♭ instead of E♮ and A♮ to turn it into C minor, and you will have a clearer idea of the difference between major and minor.

Try identifying modulations in the music you play and listen to. A change of key from major to relative minor (or vice versa) should be easy to spot once you feel confident in distinguishing major from minor. A modulation to the dominant key involves one more sharp (or one less flat) than the tonic and tends to sound much brighter than a modulation to the subdominant key, which has one less sharp (or one more flat) than the tonic, and so tends to have a rather subdued effect.

Other types of scale

Modes

Keys with the same tonic (such as C major and C minor) are sometimes said to be the major and minor modes of the same key. The word *mode* refers to the type of scale on which the music is based.

The easiest way to hear a mode is to play a series of seven consecutive notes on the white notes of a keyboard. Playing C–D–E–F–G–A–B–C gives us the Ionian mode with an interval pattern of tone, tone, semitone, tone, tone, tone, semitone. This is the same as the major scale, which is a type of mode. But there are many other types of scale in which the pattern of tones and semitones doesn't match those of the major and minor scales that we have so far studied. The term modal more usually refers to these types of scale rather than the familiar major and minor modes.

Modes were often used in music composed before 1600, after which the tonal system of major and minor keys became more popular, although much folk music remained modal. An interest in modes was revived in the late 19th century, and modal melodies (often combined with tonal harmonies) are frequently found in more recent music, including jazz, blues, rock and modern folk music.

Playing G–A–B–C–D–E–F–G creates the mixolydian mode with an interval pattern of tone, tone, semitone, tone, tone, semitone, tone. As with any other mode, the mixolydian mode can be transposed to start on any note, provided the same interval pattern is retained.

The following fiddle melody is written here in A mixolydian, or the mixolydian mode starting on A (A–B–C♯–D–E–F♯–G). When writing modal music, use the key signature which provides the best fit to the notes in the mode to avoid having to use too many accidentals. The mixolydian on A works well with a key signature of two sharps:

Trad: *Old Joe Clark*

Since this tune uses all of the notes of D major, and no other pitches, why don't we simply say it is in D major? The answer, once again, can be found in the cadences. In D major, we would expect clear perfect cadences in which the leading note (C♯) rises to the tonic (D). Here, none of the seven C♯s rise to D. The tune doesn't end on D, doesn't begin on D, and nowhere is a tonic chord of D outlined in the melody. In short, many of the key features of D major are missing. The focus of the tune is the note and chord of A - and yet this is not A major, because every G is a G♮. For all of those reasons we describe this as the mixolydian mode on A.

The scale A–B–C–D–E–F–G–A gives the notes of the Aeolian mode. This is the same as the natural minor scale that we encountered earlier in this chapter, and is the ancestor of the melodic and harmonic forms of the minor scale. The scale D–E–F–G–A–B–C–D gives the notes of the Dorian mode. Examples of traditional songs in both of these modes can be found on pages 40–41 of the *GCSE Music Literacy Workbook*.

The pentatonic scale

The pentatonic scale has five notes within each octave ('penta' means five). There are two main types of pentatonic scale. The **major pentatonic** scale uses notes 1, 2, 3, 5 and 6 of a major scale:

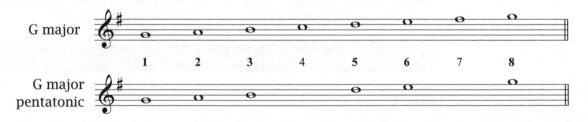

The major pentatonic is used in many familiar tunes such as *Auld Lang Syne*, *Nobody Knows the Trouble I See*, *Amazing Grace*, and *Swing Low, Sweet Chariot*. Melodies using the major pentatonic emphasise the tonic note and tonic triad of the major scale that they are derived from. This version of *Swing Low, Sweet Chariot* uses G pentatonic and emphasises the note G and the G major triad (G–B–D):

Wallace Willis: *Swing Low, Sweet Chariot*

The **minor pentatonic** scale uses notes 1, 3, 4, 5 and 7 of a natural minor scale, and emphasises the tonic note and tonic triad of the minor key:

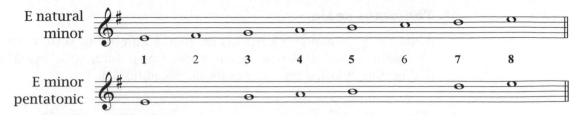

Land of the Silver Birch is written here in E minor pentatonic. Notice that much of the melody outlines an E minor triad (E–G–B):

Trad.: *Land of the Silver Birch*

The minor pentatonic often features in jazz. The opening repeated idea in Sonny Rollins' *Sonnymoon for Two* is a descending B♭ minor pentatonic scale (listen to it on the CD *Sonny Rollins: The Very Best*).

Pentatonic music is normally written using the key signature of the major or minor scale from which it is derived. Note that you can easily find a major pentatonic scale by playing up the black notes on a keyboard, starting from F♯, while a minor pentatonic scale can be found by playing up the black notes starting from E♭.

Hexatonic scales

Hexatonic scales have six notes within each octave and are often found in folk and pop melodies. One of the most common forms is the same as a major scale but without the seventh degree, as in *Twinkle, Twinkle Little Star* and *The Holly and the Ivy*.

Whole-tone scale

A different type of hexatonic scale is the whole-tone scale, which is created by using only tones and no semitones. It divides the octave into six equal divisions. A whole-tone scale can be built on any note, but will always contain the pitches of either the whole-tone scale on C or the whole-tone scale on D♭ (or their enharmonic equivalents):

A whole-tone scale doesn't have a tonic or belong to any particular key, and so is described as a whole-tone scale on C, D♭ or whatever the starting note is. It can use any combination of sharps, flats and naturals. As you cannot make major or minor triads from a whole-tone scale, there is often no clear sense of tonality in whole-tone music. However, the whole-tone scale is rarely used for complete pieces – it tends to be used mainly to give colour to particular sections of a work.

The opening of Debussy's piano prelude *Voiles* uses the whole-tone scale on C. Notice that some notes are written enharmonically – we see G♯ in bar 1 and A♭ in bar 2:

The blues scale

Although jazz and blues performers use a number of different scales, the one most commonly called the blues scale is a minor pentatonic with an added flattened fifth – it is therefore another type of hexatonic (six-note) scale:

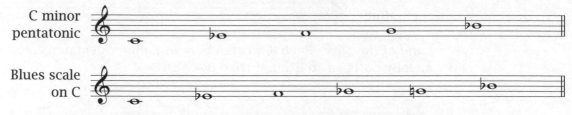

The flattened fifth is sometimes reserved for falling melodies, the same note being written enharmonically as a sharpened fourth when the melody rises:

The flattened notes in a blues scale (the third, fifth and seventh above the tonic) are often referred to as 'blue notes' and their precise pitch can be varied for expressive effect. The flat fifth, for example, might be only fractionally lower than a normal fifth, or it can be a full semitone below (as it must be on fixed-pitch instruments such as the piano). Also for expressive effect, blue notes may be approached or quitted by a short glide in pitch from above or below in order to create a 'bent note'.

Chromatic scales

A chromatic scale divides an octave into 12 semitone steps. Although you may write the notes in a chromatic scale as any combination of sharps, flats and naturals, a chromatic scale going up is best written with sharps and a chromatic scale going down with flats, as this minimises the number of accidentals required:

Chromatic scales do not have key notes and so are named after their starting note – a chromatic scale on F, on E♭ and so on. Chromatic passages are often found within pieces that are in a major or minor key, as in this famous extract from Bizet's opera *Carmen*, which is in D minor:

Bizet: 'Habanera' from *Carmen*

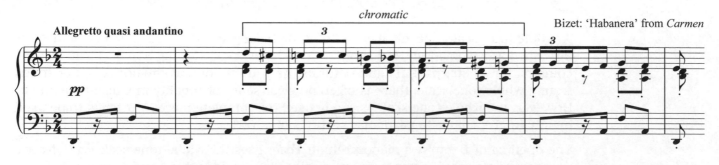

Exercise 7

1. Add three crotchets to the following to complete a whole-tone scale.

2. Name as precisely as possible the scales marked (a) and (b).

3. Name the mode of this melody and describe its rhythm.

4. Add accidentals to the notes that need them to make a blues scale on G.

Intervals

An interval is the distance in pitch between two notes. Its full description requires two parts:

➢ A number (such as a 3rd, 5th or 7th)

➢ A qualifying word (major, minor, perfect, augmented or diminished).

To identify an interval, use the following steps:

1. Imagine that the lower note in the interval is the tonic of a major scale. For example, the lower note of interval (c) in the example below is C, so the scale you are going to use is C major, even though the music is actually in the key of A♭ major.

2. Treating the lower note as 1, count up the notes of your scale until you reach the upper note. This gives you the number of the interval. For example, we count three notes for interval (c) below (C–D–E), so this is a 3rd.

3. If the upper note of the interval exactly matches the note in the major scale, then the interval is major if it is a 2nd, 3rd, 6th or 7th, or perfect if it is a 4th, 5th or octave.

4. Otherwise:

➢ If it is a semitone smaller than a major interval, it is minor

➢ If it is a semitone smaller than a perfect or minor interval, it is diminished

➢ If it is a semitone larger than a perfect or major interval, it is augmented.

In the case of interval (c), the upper note is E♭. This doesn't exactly match the third degree of C major, which is E, so it is not a major 3rd. It is a semitone less, and is therefore a minor 3rd.

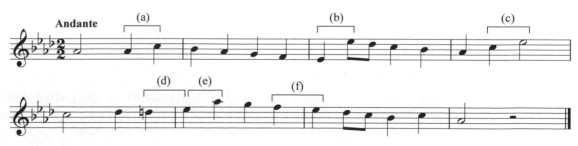

Let's apply the same process to some of the other bracketed intervals:

(a) The lower note is A♭, so count up the scale of A♭ major until you reach C, the upper note of the interval. C is the third note of the A♭ major scale, so the interval is a major 3rd.

(d) The lower note is D, so count up the scale of D major until you reach the upper note. The second note of D major is E, so this interval is a 2nd, but our upper note is E♭, a semitone less than a major 2nd. It must therefore be a minor 2nd.

(f) The lower note is E♭ – remember, always count up from the *lower* note, which may not be the first note of the interval. Count up the scale of E♭ major until you reach the upper note (F). It is the second note of the E♭ major scale, so the interval is a major 2nd.

Try naming intervals (b) and (e) for yourself.

Here are some more intervals:

Intervals (a)–(f) were all melodic intervals – in other words, one note followed the other. Interval (g) is a harmonic interval, in which both notes sound together. But it is identified in exactly the same way. Count up the major scale on its lower note (F) and you will find that B♭ is the fourth note in that scale. It is therefore a perfect 4th.

Interval (h), in which both notes are the same pitch, is called a unison.

The two notes in interval (i) *sound* exactly the same because G♭ is the enharmonic equivalent of F♯, but this is not a unison because the notes have different letter names. Count up the scale of F♯ major and you will find that its second note is G♯. Interval (i) must therefore be some kind of second. F♯ to G♯ is a major 2nd, so a minor second will be a semitone smaller (F♯ to G). However, our interval (F♯ to G♭) is a semitone smaller still, so it is a diminished 2nd.

Interval (j) is larger than an octave, but we can still use our method of counting up the major scale of its lower note. A is the 9th note of G major, so this interval is a major 9th. The numbers get rather unwieldy when describing intervals larger than this, so although (k) could be described as a major 10th, it is easier to describe it as a compound major 3rd – the word 'compound' indicating that it is an octave larger than a normal major 3rd.

Exercise 8

1. Fully describe the melodic intervals marked in this melody.

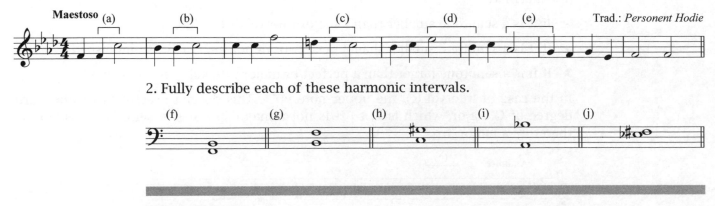

2. Fully describe each of these harmonic intervals.

Writing intervals

We can adapt the method described in the above section when writing a given interval. For instance, to find a minor 7th above middle C, count up the scale of C major to its seventh note, which is B. This note is a *major* 7th above C because it comes from the major scale, but we need a minor 7th, which is a semitone smaller. To make the interval a semitone smaller we need to make the upper note B♭, not B.

When writing intervals, always start by working out the letter name corresponding to the number and then, if it needs modifying to make the required type of interval, always use an accidental – never change the actual letter name. For instance, in the case of a 7th above C, the upper note must be a B of some kind to make the interval a 7th. If we made the upper note A♯, it would no longer be a 7th (it would be an augmented 6th), even though A♯ sounds the same as B♭.

Exercise 9

Write a note *above* each of these notes to make the named interval.

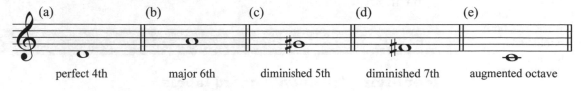

perfect 4th   major 6th   diminished 5th   diminished 7th   augmented octave

3. Reading harmony

If you want to know more about *writing* harmony, see the *AS Music Harmony Workbook* and the *A2 Music Harmony Workbook*, both published by Rhinegold.

In chapter six of the *GCSE Music Literacy Workbook* we learnt about major and minor triads in root position and inversion, and how to label them using Roman numerals or chord names. You may need to revise that chapter before working through the sections here, which deal with identifying other types of chords and understanding other aspects of harmony.

Labelling chords

Identifying triads with chord labels

Look at this example on the left. There are four chords, each with four notes.

Begin by writing down the notes of each chord in columns, ignoring any duplicates:

F	G	E	F
D	D	C	C
A	B♭	G	A

Then rearrange each column so that it consists of *alternate* letter names (such as A–C–E), reading from the bottom up:

A	D	G	C
F	B♭	E	A
D	G	C	F

You now have the root of each chord along the bottom row of your columns. Next count up the *major* scale that starts on the root (the root itself being '1'). If the note on the top row matches the 5th degree of this scale, the triad must be either major or minor. If the note in the middle row matches the third degree of this scale, the triad is major. If the note in the middle row is a semitone lower than the third degree of this scale, the triad is minor. Let's try it now, but remember that you count up from the root (the bottom note in your final table), which is not necessarily the lowest note in the actual music. All of the triads in this example are either major or minor, so we'll just look at their middle notes:

➤ The root of the first chord is D. The third note of the D major scale is F♯. We have F♮ as the middle note, so the first chord is D minor (notated as Dm).

➤ The root of the second chord is G. The third note of G major is B. We have B♭ as the middle note, so the second chord is G minor (notated as Gm).

➤ The root of the third chord is C. The third note of C major is E, which matches the middle note in our table, so the third chord is C major (notated as C).

➤ The root of the last chord is F. The third note of F major is A, which matches the middle note in our table, so the last chord is F major (notated as F).

Finally, we need to check the bottom line of our table with the bass notes in the original music. If they match, no further action is needed. If they differ, we need to add a slash to the chord symbol followed by the letter name of the actual bass note. The only place where the bass note (B♭) doesn't match the chord name (Gm) is the second chord, so this must be labelled Gm/B♭. We now have labels for all four chords, which should be written above the top stave:

Identifying triads with Roman numerals

This method is similar to using chord labels, except that it is essential to work out the key of the music first. Our example above has no accidentals, so it should be possible to identify the tonality from the key signature alone, which is F major. This is confirmed by the perfect cadence in F created by the last two chords.

Again begin by writing down the notes of each chord in columns, and then rearrange each column so that it consists of alternate notes, reading from the bottom up.

A	D	G	C
F	B♭	E	A
D	G	C	F

You now have the root of each chord along the bottom row of your columns, and you can translate these roots into Roman numerals. Uppercase Roman numerals are often used for major triads and lowercase for minor triads. Diminished triads (such as chord *vii* in the example below) are shown here in lowercase italics. Here are the notes of F major, with their Roman numerals:

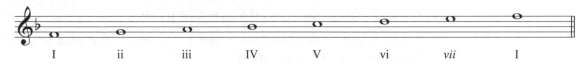

| I | ii | iii | IV | V | vi | *vii* | I |

Comparing the roots in our table (D, G, C and F) with these numerals, we can see that the four chords are vi, ii, V and I in F major.

Finally, we need to check the bottom line of our table with the bass notes in the original music. If they match, no further action is needed. Otherwise, if the bass note in the music comes from:

➤ The middle row of the table, the chord is in first inversion and so the letter 'b' must be added after its Roman numeral

➤ The top row of the table, the chord is in second inversion and so the letter 'c' must be added after its Roman numeral.

The only triad in the example that is not in root position is the second chord (ii), where the bass note is B♭. This comes from the middle row of the table, so we now know that this is chord iib.

We now have labels for all four chords. When using Roman numerals, the key should always be stated and the labels written below the bass stave.

F major: vi   iib   V   I

Whichever method of chord labelling you use, the process will seem laborious when you start, but with practice you should find that you no longer need to write down the note names and that you can juggle them in your head to achieve the correct results.

Exercise 1

Identify each chord in the following passages, using chord labels and/or Roman numerals. Remember to name the key when using Roman numerals.

1.

2.

Diminished and augmented triads

So far we have encountered two types of triad:

➤ Major triads, which contain a major 3rd above the root and can occur in any key, whether it is major or minor

➤ Minor triads, which contain a minor 3rd above the root and can occur in any key, whether it is minor or major.

In both types, the 5th above the root is always a perfect 5th. There are two other types of triad, in both of which the 5th is *not* perfect:

➤ **Diminished** triads consist of a minor 3rd plus a diminished 5th above the root

➤ **Augmented** triads consist of a major 3rd plus an augmented 5th above the root.

Chord *vii*, in both major and minor keys, is normally a diminished triad, and chord *ii* (in minor keys only) is also usually a diminished triad:

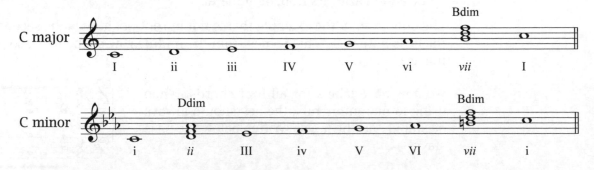

Augmented triads are less common, but chord *III* in a minor key is augmented if it includes the raised leading note of the key:

When using chord labels, add 'dim' or a small circle after the letter name of the root if a triad is diminished (e.g. Bdim or B°), and add 'aug' or + after the letter name of the root if it is augmented (e.g. E♭aug or E♭+).

Diminished and augmented triads can be inverted like any other type of chord – in fact, diminished triads are most often found in first inversion.

Exercise 2

Name the key of this passage and identify the chords by writing chord labels above the treble stave *and* Roman numerals below the bass stave:

Seventh chords

If we add a fourth note to a dominant triad, a 7th above the root, we create a **dominant 7th** chord. It is one of the most common chords of all in tonal music, frequently being used as the first chord of a perfect cadence (V^7–I) for the purpose of defining a key:

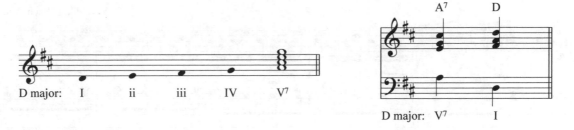

A dominant 7th is shown as V^7 when using Roman numerals. If using chord labels, add the ^{7} after the name of the basic triad (e.g. A^7). Any of the four notes of a 7th chord can appear in the bass, so the chord has a root position plus *three* inversions, which are labelled V^7b, V^7c or V^7d:

Notice how one of the notes of a 7th chord may have to be offset for clarity if the root and 7th fall on adjacent pitches.

It is possible to create a 7th chord from any triad, but for now we will look at just one other – the **supertonic 7th**. This is chord ii^7, which is often used before V^7:

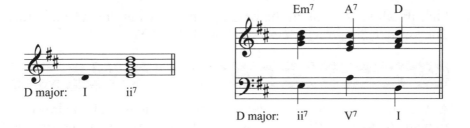

We learnt that chord *ii* in a minor key is often a diminished triad, and it follows that *ii⁷* in a minor key may also contain a diminished 5th:

Exercise 3

Name the key of this passage and identify the chords by writing chord labels above the treble stave *and* Roman numerals below the bass stave:

Broken chords

Most music does not consist of block chords that change on every note, like the examples we have looked at so far in this chapter. In the following extract, the notes of each chord are repeated in patterns of broken chords:

Vivaldi arr. Bach: Violin Concerto, Op. 4 No. 1

Despite the large number of notes, each bracketed group contains only three *different* pitches. For instance, the only pitches within the first bracket are D, F♯ and A – the tonic chord of D major. Since F♯ is in the bass, we can label this as chord Ib of D major, or D/F♯ in chord symbols.

Each bracket represents a new chord, so we can see that the harmonies change twice a bar in this example, whereas in the previous examples they changed on every beat. The rate at which chords change is known as the **harmonic rhythm**. We shall see later that the harmonic rhythm can vary within a passage, often with more rapid changes of chord as a cadence approaches.

Exercise 4

Identify all six chords in the passage above, using Roman numerals and chord labels. The key is D major and the first chord is Ib (D/F♯).

Using a chord chart

As we move on to more complex examples, you may find it helpful to make a chord chart to help you identify the harmonies. Do this by working out the key and then writing down the notes of each triad in that key – also add the 7ths in brackets for chords II[7] and V[7]. Here is a chord chart for G major (you could write the notes on a stave if you prefer):

	Inversion letter						
7th	(d)		(G)		(C)		
5th	(c)	D	E	F#	G	A	B	C
3rd	(b)	B	C	D	E	F#	G	A
Root		G	A	B	C	D	E	F#
Chord label		G	Am	Bm	C	D	Em	F#dim
Roman numeral		I	ii	iii	IV	V	vi	*vii*

When using Roman numerals, you can find the inversion letter (if needed) by seeing if the bass note of the chord occurs in row b, c or d.

Using this chord chart, let's start working out the chords in the following extract:

Bach (attributed): Menuet in G, BWV Anh. 116

The notes within the first bracket are G, B and D (with G in the bass). Our chord chart tells us that this is a tonic chord of G major in root position, so we can label it as G or chord I in G major. But the notes A and F# in the treble clef at the end of the first bar don't belong to this chord. They alert us to the fact that the harmonic rhythm changes on the last beat of bar 1, so a new chord label is needed. The notes within the second bracket are D, F# and A (with D in the bass), and our chord chart tells us that this is a chord of D major in root position, so we can label it as D or V in G major.

Exercise 5

Identify the remaining chords in the passage above, using Roman numerals and chord labels. After bar 1 there is only one chord per bar, but the last chord has just two notes. When this occurs, it is usually the 5th that is omitted, so look in your chord chart for a triad that contains A and C as the root and 3rd.

Non-chord notes (1)

While chords provide a vital element in tonal music, they are normally decorated with a variety of other notes. These non-chord notes help give shape and rhythmic interest to melodies, but they are also found in bass and accompanying parts. In the following example, the chords are labelled and non-chord notes are numbered:

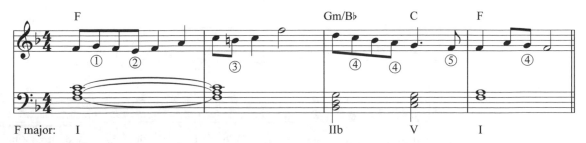

All of these non-chord notes create a momentary dissonance with the harmony being played at the same time, but because they fall on quavers between the beats, this is hardly noticeable. Notice that they all move by step between harmony notes.

① is an **upper auxiliary note** – a note that moves *up* by step from a harmony note, and then returns to the harmony note

② is a **lower auxiliary note** – a note that moves *down* by step from a harmony note, and then returns to the harmony note

③ is a **chromatic lower auxiliary note** – similar to an ordinary lower auxiliary, but involving a chromatic note, in this case B♮

④ are **passing notes** – notes that move by step between two different harmony notes

⑤ is an anticipation – a note that **anticipates** the pitch it will arrive on in the next chord.

Exercise 6

The harmony of this tune is shown by chord labels. Each chord lasts until it is replaced by a new one. Name each of the numbered types of non-chord note (e.g. 'anticipation' or 'upper auxiliary').

Trad. Cornish: *The Furry Dance*

Non-chord notes (2)

Non-chord notes that fall *on* the beat create a more obvious dissonance than the ones we looked at in the previous section. Here is the opening of *Lavender's Blue*. The notes marked ✳ are **accented passing notes**. Like unaccented passing notes, they move in step between chord notes (D, B and G).

Trad. English: *Lavender's Blue*

An **appoggiatura** (pronounced 'ap-podj-a-too-ra') is a particularly expressive on-beat dissonance because, unlike an accented passing note, it is usually approached by a leap. Notice how each appoggiatura (marked ✳) in the following example moves by step to the chord note it replaced – this chord note is called the 'resolution' of the dissonance. The second and third appoggiaturas are both chromatic:

Mozart: Violin Sonata in F, K. 547

You may sometimes see accented passing notes described as appoggiaturas if they are long and prominent. The two dissonances marked ✳ below are each longer than their resolutions, and could be regarded as appoggiaturas, even though they are approached by step like accented passing notes:

A **suspension** is an on-beat dissonance that consists of three parts:

1. The dissonant note is first 'prepared' by being sounded as a harmony note

2. This note is then repeated or sustained while the chord around it changes, creating a dissonance (this is the actual suspension)

3. Finally, it moves by step to a note of the new chord to resolve the dissonance.

Preparation (P), suspension (S) and resolution (R) are labelled in this example on the right.

When using Roman numerals, the intervals formed by the suspension and its resolution are added as superscript numerals after the chord number. When using chord labels, the suspension and its resolution are normally given separate labels. The abbreviation 'sus' (sometimes written as 'sus4') indicates that a chord contains a 4th in place of its 3rd.

Most of the non-chord notes we have discussed can be used in two or more parts at the same time. A device favoured in the Classical period was the triple suspension, in which three notes from a dominant 7th chord are suspended over a single tonic in the bass, before resolving to their own respective notes of the tonic chord:

Exercise 7

Study the following passage and then answer the questions that follow.

Mozart: *Fantasia*, K. 397

1. For how many quavers does the first note in the melody last?

2. Name the key of the passage and identify the only two chords used.

3. Name two different chromatic notes in the passage.

4. Name the type (e.g. 'anticipation' or 'upper auxiliary') of each of the five numbered non-chord notes.

Cadences

We learnt about the four main types of cadence in the *GCSE Music Literacy Workbook*, but there are some more advanced matters that we now need to discuss.

Perfect cadences

Perfect cadences are important in establishing the key of a passage, especially when the first chord is a dominant 7th. Look at chord V^7 in cadence (a) below:

> It can't occur in any major key with sharps because all such keys include F♯, and yet here we have F♮

> It can't occur in any major key with flats because all such keys include B♭, and yet here we have B♮.

The only major key that includes all of the notes of this chord is C major. The chord can also occur in C minor, as seen in cadence (b), so we also need the tonic chord to follow V^7 in order to decide whether the key is major or minor.

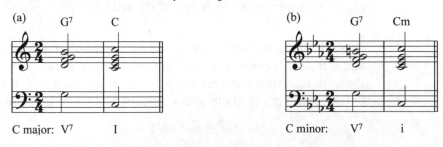

This property of V^7–I to uniquely define a key is true in every key, which is why this type of perfect cadence plays an important role in establishing new keys during the course of a piece, as explained later in this chapter.

Inverted cadences

Both chords in each cadence above are in root position, giving them particular strength. Root-position cadences of this sort are often used at the ends of important sections in a tonal piece, sometimes repeatedly at the end of a long movement. For intermediate cadences, composers often use an inverted cadence, in which one (or both) of the chords are in inversion. This creates a less conclusive effect, giving the impression that the music will continue:

C major: V⁷b   I   V   Ib   V⁷d   Ib

Feminine endings

Occasionally the final chord of a cadence can occur on a weaker beat than the first chord. This is known as a feminine ending, and examples can be seen in bars 4 and 8 of the *Soldier's March* by Schumann on page 25. Composers in the Classical period were particularly fond of feminine endings formed from the chords Ic-V to make an imperfect cadence, as in this example by Haydn:

As is often the case with a second inversion, Ic hardly seems to be a chord in its own right – this example could be regarded as decoration of chord V, with the bracketed notes forming a double suspension, prepared at the end of bar 3 and resolved on the last chord of the extract.

Phrygian cadence

One other cadence that you may encounter is the Phrygian cadence – it is simply a special type of imperfect cadence in a minor key, formed from chords IVb-V.

Tierce de Picardie

Passages in a minor key sometimes conclude with a cadence that ends with a major tonic chord to give a better sense of completion. This is known as a *tierce de Picardie* (French for Picardy third). The term may refer to the Picardy region in France, but it is probably derived from the Old French word *picart*, which can mean 'sharp' – a reference to the 3rd of the final chord being raised to make it major.

Exercise 8

Study the passage below and then answer the questions that follow.

1. Name the key of this passage.

2. Is the cadence inverted or in root position?

3. Identify the type of cadence as precisely as possible.

4. What is the name of the rhythmic device in bars 2–3?

Chord progressions

Chord Ic before a perfect cadence is often called a cadential $\frac{6}{4}$, because it consists of pitches that are a (compound) 4th and 6th above the root.

A chord progression (or harmonic progression) is a series of chords played in succession. Cadences are progressions, even though they consist of only two chords. However, most cadences are introduced by an approach chord of some sort. For instance, a very common cadential progression is ii⁷b–V⁷–I.

Another common cadential progression is Ic–V–I, which is often found in music of the Classical period – it was one of the few occasions when second-inversion triads were used and, as we saw in the Haydn example on the previous page, it can be reduced to Ic–V when an imperfect cadence is required.

Most chord progressions are longer than these, though. You may perhaps know the 12-bar blues progression, which has several variants based around a pattern of three four-bar phrases with the harmonies I–I–I–I, IV–IV–I–I, V–IV–I–I.

For information on the chromatic circle of 5ths, see the section on secondary dominants on p.46.

One of the most common longer progressions is the circle of 5ths. We saw on page 22 that this term is used to describe how keys are related, but a circle of 5ths *chord progression* normally consists of chords whose roots are a 5th apart, rather than keys whose tonics are a 5th apart. There could still be 12 possible chords, but composers generally use a shortened version called the **diatonic circle of 5ths**, which passes through all seven triads of a key, without any chromatic notes:

Notice that the root of each chord is a perfect 5th below (or perfect 4th above) the one before, except at the bracket, where the interval is an *augmented* 4th – this forms a 'short circuit' that allows the progression to return to the tonic before any chromatic notes are introduced.

Even the diatonic circle of 5ths does not often appear in its entirety – composers frequently prefer to use just part of it, such as the progression iii–vi–ii–V–I.

Modulation

Although music can modulate to any key, most works written in the period between about 1600 and 1830 (and many later pieces, too) rarely stray beyond a small range of related keys (i.e. those involving only a few new accidentals). We can see which these are by looking at the diagram of keys, to which relative minor keys have been added as an inner circle:

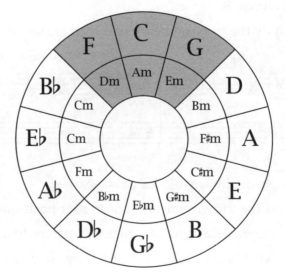

Related keys are those that are next to each other in the circle. So, if a piece is in C major, it might modulate to the dominant (G), the subdominant (F), and the relative minors of the tonic (Am), dominant (Em) and subdominant (Dm).

Similarly, if a piece is in A minor, it might modulate to the dominant (Em), the subdominant (Dm), and the relative majors of the tonic (C), dominant (G) and subdominant (F).

Another type of key change that you may encounter is between tonic major and tonic minor (sometimes known as the parallel major and minor keys), such as from A minor to A major. As you can see from the diagram above, these two keys are not closely related and so there is often not a modulation – instead, the music abruptly changes mode from minor to major, or vice versa.

Pieces that modulate once will almost certainly modulate again, if only to return to the tonic before the end (although this may not be apparent if an exam question is based on just an extract from a longer piece, as is often the case).

If you use chord labels to identify chords, no special action is needed after a modulation, since chord labels refer only to the current chord and not to the key. However, Roman numerals have to be written in the *new* key because the tonic (I) and all of the other degrees of the scale will have changed.

Modulations often involve a **pivot chord** - a chord that is common to both the old key and the new. When this occurs, the chord concerned should be labelled in both the old key and the new, with the name of the new key clearly marked:

D major: Ib *viib* I ii vic
B minor: ic V i V⁷d ib *ii⁷b* ic V⁷ i

Once the music has modulated you can expect to see the accidentals of the new key being used and a cadence to confirm that new key, as above.

Exercise 9

Study the following passage and then answer the questions below.

S.S. Wesley: *Wetherby*

1. Name the key of each of the four bracketed phrases.

2. What type of cadence is used at the end of phrase 1?

3. Show precisely how the pivot chord on the first beat of bar 5 should be labelled when using Roman numerals.

4. Name the type of non-chord note marked **A** in bar 5 and **B** in bar 6.

5. Which bar starts with a double suspension in the top two parts?

6. Give the number of one bar in which a cadential $\frac{6}{4}$ occurs on the second beat.

Chromatic chords

Chromatic chords are those that contain one or more notes outside the current key. Listen carefully to the difference between these two progressions:

If you use only your *eyes*, you could be misled into thinking that the second of these passages modulates to G major. But if you use your *ears*, it should be clear from the cadence made by the last two chords that the key is C major. Rather than triggering a modulation, the chord of D major seems to strengthen this cadence. This is because D is the dominant of G, which in turn is the dominant of C. For that reason, this particular chord is often called 'the dominant of the dominant', and is frequently found as an approach chord to a perfect cadence. In the second example above, notice how the chromatic alteration of the 3rd in chord II is shown when using Roman numerals. An alternative method is shown in the next example.

Other triads can be chromatically altered in a similar way, and are known by the family name of **secondary dominants**, because each is a dominant of the *chord* that follows (not the dominant of a new *key*). Minor 7ths are often added above the root, to enhance this dominant-like effect:

Scott Joplin and Louis Chauvin: *Heliotrope Bouquet*

This pattern of chords is sometimes called the ragtime progression, although it can be found in many other types of music.

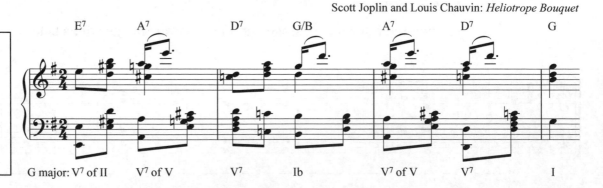

Look at the first four chords in this example: E⁷–A⁷–D⁷–G. Can you see that their roots are a 5th apart? However, unlike the diatonic circle of 5ths we discussed earlier (where similar chords would be Em–Am–D–G), here each chord is major, and has a 7th. This is a **chromatic circle of 5ths** – and the word chromatic is important, because there is no modulation involved. The entire chain of chords simply strengthens the perfect cadence in G major with which the progression ends.

Exercise 10

Study the music below and then answer the questions that follow.

Schubert: Waltz, Op. 9b No. 3

1. Identify the chords in this passage using both chord labels and Roman numerals. The key is G major and there is one chord per bar, except in bar 6 where there are two chords.

2. What type of chord is used in bars 1 and 4?

3. Which bar starts with a cadential $^6_4$?

4. Name the rhythmic device used in the melody in bars 1–2 and 4–5.

The diminished 7th

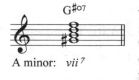

A diminished 7th chord consists of four notes that are each a minor 3rd apart – its outer notes form the interval of a diminished 7th. It can occur as a diatonic chord in minor keys (chord *vii*[7]), as shown on the left, but it is also frequently found as a chromatic chord, in which case it is labelled as simply 'dim.7' when using Roman numerals. Its symmetrical nature means that there is no effective difference between inversions, so inversion letters are not normally added, unless it is identified as *vii*[7]. When using chord labels, either 'dim7' or °[7] is added after the chord's letter name.

The Neapolitan 6th

A Neapolitan 6th chord is the first inversion of a major chord on the flattened supertonic (♭IIb) of a key – often a minor key:

Greene: *Lord, Let me Know Mine End*

Neapolitan refers to Naples, the Italian city where composers first made great use of the chord in the Baroque period, and 6th refers to the fact that it is a first-inversion chord, containing the interval of a 6th (and, of course, a 3rd) above its bass note.

The augmented 6th

An augmented 6th chord is based around the interval of an augmented 6th between its outer notes. Most commonly, the lower of these is a semitone above the dominant, and the upper is a semitone below the dominant in a higher octave. These two notes move outwards by a semitone to the dominant in the next chord, which is normally either V or Ic. The inner notes of an augmented 6th chord can be any of the following:

German augmented 6th: French augmented 6th: Italian augmented 6th:

C major: Aug.6   V   Aug.6   V   Aug.6   V

The names German, French and Italian don't have any special significance, but if you are required to label the precise type of augmented 6th – and you know your geography – it can help to remember that the second note from the top is highest in the German 6th (the most northerly of the three countries), a semitone lower in the French 6th (south of Germany) and a tone lower still in the Italian 6th (the most southerly of the three countries).

The chord is normally identified as 'aug.6', even when using Roman numerals, but when using chord labels, augmented 6ths are often enharmonically notated – for example, the German 6th above would be labelled A♭⁷. This is because the chord, *in isolation*, sounds like the dominant 7th of D♭ (A♭–C–E♭–G♭). However, it is important not to think of it in these terms when analysing music – all three examples above are chromatic chords in C major, and are nothing to do with D♭ major.

Exercise 11

Study this extract and then complete the blanks in the commentary that follows.

Haydn: 'The Heavens are Telling' from *The Creation*

Try to listen to this final chorus from the first part of Haydn's oratorio *The Creation*, and note the thrilling effect of the chromatic harmonies above at the climax of the movement.

This passage is in the key of .... and it starts on the .... inversion of a dominant 7th chord. There is a double .... at the start of bar 2. The chord in bar 3 is a(n) .... , which is followed by a(n) .... chord in bar 4. The perfect cadence at the end of the extract begins with a .... in bar 5. The bass note B at the end of bar 2 is a ....

Other types of chord

➤ **Added 6th chords**, which are common in jazz, are formed by adding a 6th above the root to a major or minor triad (see example (a) below).

➤ **Major 7th chords** consist of a major triad with a major 7th added. For example, C^maj7 consists of the notes C, E, G and B (see (b) below). It is important to use 'maj7' in the chord label to distinguish such chords from normal 7th chords, which have a minor 7th.

➤ The dominant 7th can be extended to a dominant 9th (major or minor), 11th (perfect) or 13th (major or minor) by adding further 3rds to the chord. Usually, some notes (printed in smaller type in (c) below) are omitted from these thick-textured chords, but they normally include the root, 3rd, 7th and the named interval (9th, 11th or 13th):

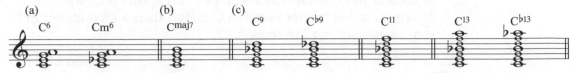

Many of these chords are mainly used in jazz, rock, pop and light music. In classical harmony, discords such as a major 7th or minor 9th usually arise from the addition of non-chord notes, such as appoggiaturas and suspensions. They therefore don't form part of the normal system of Roman numerals, but if necessary they can be shown by adding figures and accidentals to the appropriate Roman numeral, such as $V^{\flat 9}$.

Other harmonic features of music

Pedal

A pedal point (usually shortened to pedal) is a sustained or repeated note heard against changing chords. Pedals are usually on the dominant or the tonic. A pedal on both notes is called a double pedal.

Pedals are often in the bass – a pedal in the topmost part is called an inverted pedal and a pedal in the middle of the texture is called an inner pedal. A pedal may be decorated with non-chord notes (often auxiliary notes).

The chords heard against a pedal often form a progression of their own, which can be identified independently. In the following example, the progression is I–iib–V⁷c–I, with the tonic pedal on E being dissonant with the chords in bars 2 and 3:

Beethoven: Piano Sonanta in E, Op.14 No. 1

The addition of '/I' to chords iib and V⁷c indicates that these chords are heard against a tonic pedal.

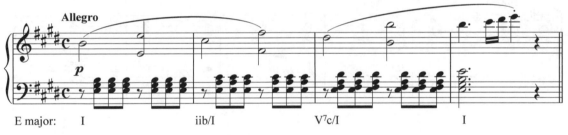

E major: I   iib/I   V⁷c/I   I

False relation

The term false relation describes the effect produced by the natural and chromatically altered versions of the same pitch used in different parts at either (a) the same time, or (b) in close proximity:

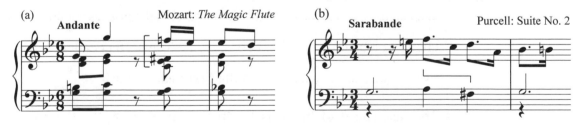

Remember that a false relation can only occur between different parts. So, the clash between F♮ and F♯ in both these examples is a false relation, but the use of B♮ and B♭ is not, since these pitches occur in the same part in both examples.

Harmonic sequence

A sequence is the immediate repetition of an idea at a higher or lower pitch. In a harmonic sequence, a chord pattern is immediately repeated at a different pitch – the melody will often be sequential as well, as in the examples below. In the first extract (which we encountered earlier in the chapter), the chord pattern of bar 1 is repeated a step higher in bar 2, and a step higher again in bar 3, but the entire sequence stays in the key of D major. The second extract shows a modulating sequence, in which the progression V–I is first heard in C major, then a step higher in D minor, and finally a step higher still, in E minor:

Vivaldi arr. Bach: Violin Concerto, Op. 4 No. 1

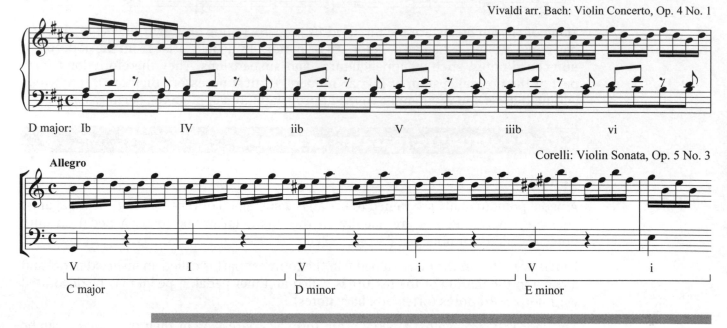

D major: Ib   IV   iib   V   iiib   vi

Corelli: Violin Sonata, Op. 5 No. 3

V   I   V   i   V   i

C major   D minor   E minor

Exercise 12

Study the music below and then complete the blanks in the commentary that follows.

Bach: *Magnificat*

This passage begins in the key of .... The chord in bar 1 is a(n) .... triad, and the first chord in bar 2 is decorated with the type of non-chord note known as a(n) .... The second chord in bar 2 is a(n) .... , and this same chord appears again, but with an enharmonic change, on beat .... of bar .... The perfect cadence in bars 3–4 is approached by a .... on the first beat of bar 3.

The last chord of bar 4 is IV⁷ in the opening key of the passage, but it is a pivot chord and therefore should also be numbered as .... in the key of .... , the key in which the passage ends. This new key is the .... of the opening key. Chord V in the final perfect cadence is decorated with another .... , this time in the topmost part.

4. Notating performance techniques

Most of this chapter is about the more unusual symbols in notation, but we will begin by looking at a range of signs that can be used to indicate articulation – in other words, ways to show precisely how notes should be played.

Slurs and phrase marks

A curved line drawn over a complete phrase is called a phrase mark, as seen in the following example. It tells the pianist to play the chords smoothly, so that they sound together like a complete musical statement.

Debussy: *La Cathédrale engloutie*

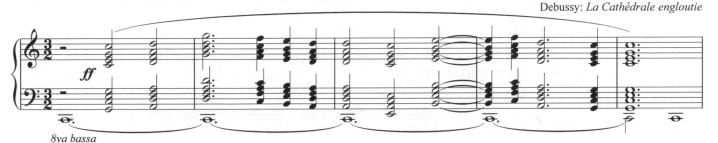

8va bassa

> Remember that the curved lines in the bass part are ties, because they join notes of the same pitch.

In vocal and wind music, a phrase mark usually indicates that the notes should be performed in one breath. A slur can be drawn over a few notes to indicate that these are to be played smoothly or legato. In vocal music, a slur may also be written over a melisma, where several notes are sung to one syllable.

Articulation marks

The following signs affect the precise length of a note, without changing the regularity of the beat, and are normally written as close to the note head as possible:

A staccato dot means that the note is to be played shorter than a similar unmarked note, while a staccatissimo wedge means that the note should be played as short as possible. The combination of staccato dots with slurs means mezzo staccato ('half staccato') – play the notes only a little shorter than normal. Tenuto implies making a note stand out by holding it for its full length, and also possibly giving it a slight stress (which may in fact mean slightly shortening the previous note). The final symbol is often found in cymbal and harp parts and it indicates that the note should continue sounding until it dies away naturally. It may be accompanied by the words 'let ring' or their French equivalent *laissez vibrer* (abbreviated to *l.v.*).

The following signs indicate that a note should be played with additional force:

The arrowhead signs for accents are written above or below the stave, on the note-head side of the note whenever possible, and always point forward. They indicate a note to be played with a greater sense of attack than unmarked notes. An alternative is to write *sf* (short for *sforzato*, Italian for 'forced'). The direction *fp* means that after a loud attack the volume should immediately drop to a quiet level – something that is more effective on long notes.

The v-like signs for marcato are also written above or below the stave, on the note-head side of the note whenever possible, but they point up when above the stave and down when below. They imply a stronger attack than a simple accent. The abbreviations *fz* or *sfz* can be used instead – there is no clear distinction between these and *sf*, since they are all based on similar Italian words. However, these abbreviations can be expanded to forms such as *sffz*, when it is necessary to indicate a very loud accent in the middle of an already loud passage.

The articulation marks discussed above can be combined, providing they don't conflict. One possible combination is staccato and marcato. In such a case, the sign affecting the length of the note is written closest to the note head:

If a particular pattern of articulation continues for many notes, the symbols can be shown in just the first bar or two, after which the word *simile* (Italian for 'similar') or the abbreviation *sim.* can be written to indicate that the pattern continues.

Instrumental techniques

Tremolo

Further information about instrumental techniques (including sound clips) can be found at www. philharmonia.co.uk/ thesoundexchange/ or www.bbc.co.uk/ orchestras/guide/.

A tremolo is the rapid repetition of a single pitch or a fast alternation between two or more different pitches:

Tremolo strings can be heard accompanying the swan theme (Act 2, No. 10) in Tchaikovsky's *Swan Lake*.

In the first type ((a) above), the main note shows how long the effect is to last while the number of tremolo beams indicates how to divide the note. One beam means play the note as repeated quavers, two beams indicate repeated semiquavers and so on. At fast speeds, three or more beams usually indicate that the note should be repeated as many times as possible without counting the number of repetitions.

When writing the second type ((b) above), both notes are given the full length of the tremolo and are joined by one main beam (even if they are crotchets or minims), with additional beams drawn between the notes but without touching the stems. The total number of beams again indicates the speed of the repetitions.

The horn section can be heard using flutter tonguing in variation 10 of *Don Quixote* by Richard Strauss.

A special tremolo effect called flutter-tonguing can be produced on some woodwind and brass instruments by rolling an r while blowing. This is written as a tremolo with the instruction flutter tongue (*flatterzunge* in German).

Mutes

In music for strings and brass, *con sordino* or *con sord.* (Italian for 'with mute') instructs a player to use a mute. The direction *senza sordino* or *senza sord.* ('without mute') means return to playing without a mute.

Muted strings can be heard accompanying the solo horn and flute soon after the start of the last movement of Brahms' Symphony No. 1.

Brass players can use a range of differently shaped mutes for specific sound effects. The jazz trumpeter Miles Davies can be heard using a Harmon mute in 'Will o' the Wisp' and 'Pan Piper' on his album *Sketches of Spain*. The trombonists in the Glenn Miller Orchestra use plunger mutes to create a wah-wah sound in *Tuxedo Junction*.

A horn player can also hand-stop a note to create a muted effect, and this is marked *chiuso* (Italian for 'closed') in the music, or individual notes may be marked with a cross.

Harmonics

Almost every sound we hear comprises a fundamental tone and a series of harmonics or overtones. Our ears hear these elements as a single sound. The relative volume of each harmonic within the overall sound contributes to its timbre or tone quality, and helps us to distinguish between the same note played on, say, a clarinet and an oboe.

String players, harpists and guitarists can make a harmonic sound instead of the normal note by lightly pressing a particular point on a string while playing. The result sounds pure and thin in comparison with the normal note.

There are two types of harmonic. A **natural harmonic** is played by lightly touching an open string, while an **artificial harmonic** (which is not possible on the harp) is played by stopping the string in the normal way with one finger, and then using another finger to lightly touch the string at a place that will produce the required harmonic.

The most common harmonic used on bowed string instruments sounds two octaves above the fundamental note – it can be heard throughout Variation 10 of Paganini's Caprice No. 24 for solo violin. Harmonics are indicated by a circle over the required sounding note ((a) below), or as the fundamental note with the position to lightly touch the string shown by a diamond shaped note ((b) below). In the latter case, the desired sounding pitch may also be indicated, as in (c):

(a)   (b)   (c)

On the harp, a harmonic is indicated by a small circle over the fundamental note, which then sounds an octave higher when played:

Debussy: *Nuages*

[Modéré]

These harmonics...   sound at these pitches.

The guitar can play natural harmonics an octave higher than the open string (at the 12th fret), an octave and a fifth higher (7th fret), two octaves higher (5th fret), and two octaves and a major third higher (4th or 9th fret). Artificial harmonics can also be created on any fretted note to likewise sound an octave higher, an octave and a fifth higher, and so on.

In staff notation, harmonics are usually written using a diamond note head at the pitch to be stopped – sometimes, the sounding notes will also be written in brackets above the stave. In guitar tablature a variety of methods are used – one common one is to write the fret number to be stopped with a diamond drawn around it for a natural harmonic, and a triangle drawn around it for an artificial harmonic. However, many different methods are used and it's best to include a key to any tab you create for the guitar. (For more on guitar tab see page 54.)

Glissando

A glissando or portamento is a slide between notes. The effect is notated as a slanting straight or wavy line, sometimes accompanied by the abbreviation 'gliss'.

Strictly speaking, a portamento is a continuous glide in pitch between notes, while in a glissando the individual pitches can be heard (as when running your fingers across a keyboard), but the two terms are often used interchangeably.

Writing for guitar

Stave notation

When stave notation is used for the guitar, it is written in the treble clef, but sounds an octave lower than written. The figure *8* at the bottom of the clef below is a reminder of this. A standard acoustic or electric guitar has six strings, tuned to the following notes:

The neck of the guitar is fretted, with the first fret being nearest to the tuning pegs. Each fret is a semitone above the one before. If you play an open G string it sounds as a G, but if you press down on the first fret before playing, it will sound as G♯ (or A♭). If you press the fifth fret on the D string, it will sound a G, the same pitch as the G string above.

Stave notation for the bass guitar is written in the bass clef, but again the notes sound an octave lower than written. The four strings are tuned an octave lower than the bottom four strings on a normal guitar (to the same notes as the double bass):

The bass guitar also has frets at semitone intervals, although players with a good ear sometimes prefer the fretless bass, where the precise pitches have to be learned from experience, like those on the cello and double bass.

Guitar tab

Tab is an abbreviation of tablature, a word referring to its table-like appearance. The use of tablature dates back to medieval times, and for several centuries it remained the preferred way of notating music for plucked-string instruments such as the lute.

Today, guitar tab is commonly used in jazz, rock and pop. The notes to play are shown by their fingering. Six horizontal lines represent the strings of a standard guitar, with the lowest at the bottom. The numbers on each line show which fret to press to make the required note. Tab can be written with or without an indication of the rhythm, but if it is included then it uses a similar system to staff notation with a time signature at the start, headless notes above the fret numbers to show lengths, and rests included where necessary. Tab does not need key signatures or accidentals. The fret hand (left hand) plays the numbers and the right hand plays the rhythm.

> If you want to use tab for an exam composition, first check with your teacher that this is acceptable to the exam board concerned. If allowed, it is likely that you will be expected to notate the rhythm above the tablature.

The tab here shows that the piece starts with two quavers: fret 3 on the B string (which is D) followed by fret 2 (which is C♯). Then comes a crotchet chord made up of fret 2 on the A string (which is B) plus D and upper B (both on open strings, shown by '0').

When fret numbers are lined up vertically, the notes are played simultaneously, like a chord in staff notation. Because many notes on the guitar have alternative fingerings (using a higher fret on a lower string), those shown above are not the only possibilities.

Bass guitar tab is written on four lines, representing the four strings of the bass guitar, with the bottom line being the lowest string (E). The following part starts with quavers on D (open string) and C♯ (fret 4 on the A string), followed by a crotchet on B (fret 2 on the A string), and so on.

If the strings of a guitar are to be tuned to non-standard pitches, then the new tuning is written at the start of the music, with the pitches to which the guitar should be tuned written as letter names against each line of the tab.

Guitar frames

Guitar chords can also be written as frames or grids. Here the six strings of the guitar are drawn vertically, with the lowest E string on the left. In the example shown here, the X above this string indicates that it is not played. The other symbols show that the guitarist is to play:

➢ C (fret 3 on the A string)

➢ E (fret 2 on the D string)

➢ G (an open string, shown by the small circle)

➢ C (fret 1 on the B string)

➢ E (another open string).

The next example shows a barre chord (or bar chord), in which the index finger presses down on fret 2 across multiple strings while the other three fingers are positioned on fret 4 as shown. Reading from the left, the lowest E string is not played, and the other five strings produce a chord of B major:

➢ B (fret 2 on the A string)

➢ F♯ (fret 4 on the D string)

➢ B (fret 4 on the G string)

➢ D♯ (fret 4 on the B string)

➢ F♯ (fret 2 on the E string).

> As with guitar tab, rhythmic details should be included with guitar grids when writing a composition for an exam.

In a pop, rock or jazz group the chords are normally played by rhythm guitar, and the melody or solo line by lead guitar. The rhythm guitar part may include a strum pattern to show the style required. On a down stroke, shown by a downward arrow, the strings sound from high to low. The reverse occurs with an up stroke. Down strokes are more emphatic than up strokes, and so various combinations of strokes can be used to create different rhythmic effects. A precise indication of the rhythm may also accompany the strum pattern:

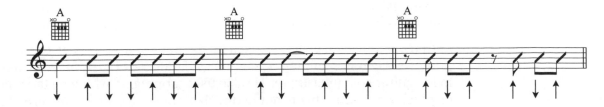

Exercise 1

Play the following melody and bass line on guitars or on any suitable instrument(s). If you are a guitarist, also try playing the chords shown by the grids.

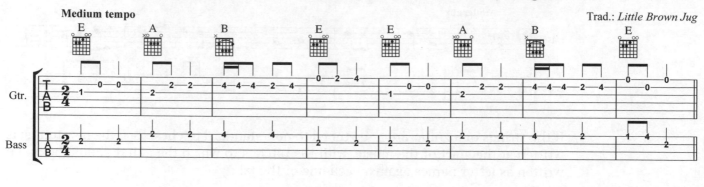

Medium tempo

Trad.: *Little Brown Jug*

Special guitar techniques

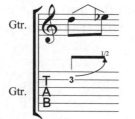

A **bend** is played by picking a note with the right hand, and then pushing the string sideways with the left hand to alter the pitch as it sounds. Brian May makes extensive use of pitch bends during his guitar solo in *I Want to Break Free* by Queen (from around 2 minutes). In staff notation a bend is written as an angled slur, and in tab by a curved arrow or the letter 'b'. The interval which the note is bent can be marked as '½' for a semitone or 'full' for a tone.

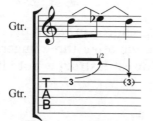

In a **bend and release** (or release bend) the string is allowed to return to the original note after the bend. This is notated as an upward bend followed by a downward one. In tab, where the effect can be marked 'r', the final note is usually written in brackets because it is not actually played with the picking hand.

A **slide** is played by plucking a note and then sliding the left finger up or down to a new note on the same string. The bass player Herbie Flowers plays slides in Lou Reed's single *Take a Walk on the Wild Side*. The effect is notated as a short glissando line between the two notes.

Vibrato can be applied to a note by rolling a finger back and forth across a fret. It can be shown by a wavy horizontal line above the note(s) or the letter 'v' in tab. On an electric guitar, vibrato can be produced with a tremolo arm (often called a 'whammy bar') – a lever that allows the tension of the strings to be quickly varied, and that can also be used for wider pitch bends.

In a **hammer-on**, a left finger is brought down on a string already sounding to cause a higher pitch to be heard. The opposite is a **pull-off**, in which a left finger is lifted while a string is sounding, causing a lower pitch to be heard. Both pitches are notated and slurred together, and may be marked 'h' for a hammer-on or 'p' for a pull-off.

Both techniques are generally used in fast passages – hammer-ons when ascending and pull-offs when descending. The guitarist Eddie Van Halen makes extensive use of both in his guitar solo in *Eruption*. He also uses **tapping**, in which he taps the strings (instead of plucking them). This is notated with + above the notes concerned in staff notation, or 't' in tab.

Writing for percussion

The percussion clef

A percussion clef indicates that the lines and spaces on the stave represent different sounds of indefinite pitch. The stave itself usually contains five lines if the part shows all the instruments in a drum kit, but if an instrument produces a single tone, like the castanets, then it can be given just one line. If it produces several tones, or the player is using several instruments, then more lines will be needed:

In a drum-kit part each instrument is allocated a particular space or line on the stave, with higher sounding instruments at the top. The note heads for metal instruments are written as crosses (or diamonds for white notes):

| Crash cymbal | Hi-hat cymbal | Tomtom 1 | Tomtom 2 | Snare drum | Tomtom 3 | Bass drum |

The allocation of instruments to lines and spaces is usually as shown above, but the positioning of any additional instruments on the stave is less standard. If there is any doubt, a drum-kit legend can be used to show how the lines and spaces are allocated.

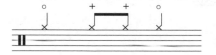

The hi-hat cymbal can be played with the plates open (o) or closed (+). These symbols can be added above the notes to show the different sounds required.

A drum-kit part usually shows just a bar or two of each rhythm, followed by indications of how it is to be repeated. Special features, such as introductions and endings, are notated in full. Short solos at the ends of phrases may be notated, or the word 'fill' can be used to instruct the player to improvise something appropriate. The words 'ad lib.' invite the drummer to embellish the basic rhythm pattern.

In the following drum-kit part, the symbol ⫰ means repeat the previous two bars, and is written across the central barline of each pair of bars. The symbol ✗ means repeat the previous bar, and is written in the middle of the bar. Instructions tell the drummer the rhythmic style or 'groove' of the music (a cha-cha-cha is a type of Latin-American dance music that became popular in the 1950s), and any particular effects required. 'Cross stick' means placing the drumstick across the head of the drum, with the tip resting on the skin – the sound is then made by striking the shaft of the stick on the rim of the drum opposite the tip to create a dry, clicking sound, rather like claves. This part has been notated with diamond-shaped note heads. Finally, in the solo that begins in the last two bars, the symbol ╱ has been used as a place marker for the crotchet beats in each bar:

Rolls

Timpani parts are often written without a key signature, but the notes to which the drums are tuned are usually written at the start of the music.

A roll is a rapid succession of strokes that are played fast enough to give the impression of a sustained sound. It can be notated by either tremolo beams or a trill sign (followed by a wavy line if the roll extends over more than one note):

Strictly speaking, a roll is not a trill because it doesn't consist of two different pitches, but rolls have been indicated by a trill sign for hundreds of years. Rolls can be played on other percussion instruments, including the large orchestral bass drum and the side drum (an orchestral snare drum).

Special string techniques

Players of the violin, viola, cello and double bass can use a variety of techniques, many of which have special notation or text markings. When using the bow, the player has a choice of a either a down bow (which can be marked ⊓) or an up bow (which can be marked ⋁). A down bow starts from the end of the bow in which it is held and tends to produce a stronger sound than an up bow, which starts at the end of the bow farthest from the player's hand. In string music, a slur indicates that notes are to be played in a single bow stroke. For example, bars 1 and 3 in the following melody for double bass:

would be played like this:

Unless you are an experienced string player, it is best to leave bowing to the players. Composers usually only add bowing marks when they want a specific effect, like the repeated heavy down bows played by strings in 'The Augers of Spring: Dances of the Young Girls' in Stravinsky's *Rite of Spring*.

Listen to the strings playing pizzicato throughout Johann Strauss' *Pizzicato Polka*.

The word *pizzicato* or abbreviation *pizz.* indicates that the strings should be plucked with the right hand. A return to bowing is shown by the word *arco*. Three- or four-note pizzicato chords can be played by strumming the strings, and are notated with arrows indicating the strumming pattern or with up and down bow signs. The instruction *alla guitara* or *quasi guitara* ('like a guitar') might also be added.

The left hand is also sometimes used to play pizzicato, and this is indicated with a cross over or under the note:

Paganini: Caprice No. 24, Variation No. 9

A percussive sound, known as a snap pizzicato, is created when a string is plucked vigorously enough for it to snap back against the fingerboard. Snap pizzicato is found in the music of such 20th-century composers as Bartók, where it is shown with the symbol ⊘. It can also be heard in the 'slap bass' playing of much early rock and roll, and rockabilly, where it was used to make the unamplified string bass sound as loud as possible.

Col legno requires the player to turn over the bow and strike the string with the wood of the bow. The direction *sul ponticello* (or *sul pont.*) means play with the bow close to the bridge. This creates a thin, whispering tone as it emphasises the higher harmonics in the sound. The opposite effect is *sul tasto*, where the player bows over or close to the fingerboard to create a warm, rich sound, lacking in higher harmonics.

Double stopping

Double or triple stopping means playing two or three notes simultaneously on a bowed string instrument. Take care that the notes are playable if you use this technique when composing. For example, look at the chords in the following:

Bach: 'Sarabande' from Suite No. 1 in G

Violoncello

The strings of a cello are tuned to these notes and only one note at a time can be played on each string.

The first chord in bar 1 is played with the G and D strings as open strings, and the note B is played on the A string. Had the B been an octave lower, the chord would not have been playable.

Although four-note chords for string instruments are sometimes seen, they are performed as very fast arpeggios ('spread chords') because four strings cannot be played simultaneously.

Writing for the piano

In piano music, the right hand generally plays the music written on the upper stave and the left hand plays the notes written on the lower. However, certain points in the music might be labelled *m.d.* (Italian: *mano destra*) or R.H., indicating that the right hand should be used, and *m.s.* (*mano sinistra*) or L.H., meaning that the left hand should be used (see the example by Beethoven on the next page).

Piano pedalling

Most pianos have two pedals. The right-hand one is the sustaining pedal and allows the sound to continue after the fingers have left the keys, by raising the dampers on the strings. The instruction *con pedale* ('with the pedal') or *con ped.* means that it should be used in whatever way the pianist decides best. Alternatively, the places where the pedal is to be pressed and released may be precisely notated in any one of the following ways:

The left-hand or soft pedal mutes the sound by moving the hammers so that they are either closer to the strings or so they strike fewer strings per note. This is notated with the instruction *una corda* ('one string') and cancelled by *tre corde* ('three strings').

Octave signs

Octave signs can minimise the number of leger lines used in very high or very low passages. *8* or *8va* (short for *ottava*, Italian for 'octave') placed above a passage in the treble clef means play the notes an octave higher than written. The same sign placed *below* a passage in the bass clef means play the notes an octave lower than written, although *8va bassa* (abbreviated to *8ba* or *8vb*) is often preferred to avoid confusion.

The expression *coll' 8va* means 'with the octave' – in other words, play the written notes *and* double them at the octave. It's an instruction that is mainly found in piano music, since pianists can play in octaves relatively easily. If it is written over a treble stave it means that the notes should be doubled an octave higher, while if it appears below a bass stave, the notes should be doubled an octave lower. Again, the latter is less ambiguous if expressed as *coll' 8va bassa*.

In all of these cases, the extent of the passage concerned can be shown with an extender line made up of dashes, as shown below. The music returns to its written pitch at the end of the octave line, or where the music is marked *loco* (Italian for 'normal place'):

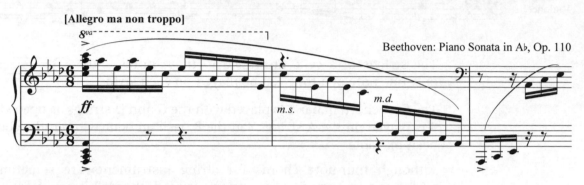

Beethoven: Piano Sonata in A♭, Op. 110

Arpeggio sign

An arpeggio sign is a vertical wavy line placed before a chord to indicate that its notes are to be played in quick succession (as a 'spread chord') rather than at the same time. Sometimes the arpeggio sign includes an arrow head to show the direction in which the notes should be played, but otherwise the chord is usually arpeggiated upwards. Arpeggiated chords can be written for any instrument that can play chords. In piano music, they are used when a chord is too wide to play all its notes simultaneously:

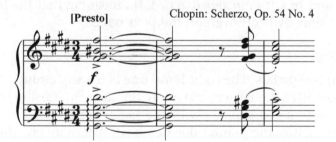

Chopin: Scherzo, Op. 54 No. 4

or for special effects, such as if the piano is to imitate the guitar or harp.

Ornaments

Ornaments to decorate a melodic line can be written in by composers or, in older styles of music, they may be added by performers, in keeping with the conventions of the age from which the music comes.

The acciaccatura

An acciaccatura (pronounced 'at-chak-ka-too-ra') is written as a grace note (a small note with a stroke through its tail, that may be joined to the main note with a slur). An acciaccatura has no rhythmic value of its own and, depending on the style of the music, may be played just before the beat, on the beat and followed immediately by the main note, or simultaneously with the main note:

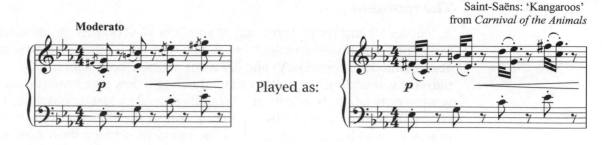

Played as:

Other grace notes

You may see several grace notes in small type printed before a main note. Generally these are played as fast as possible before the main note, which is usually played on the beat:

Chopin: Scherzo, Op. 20 No. 1

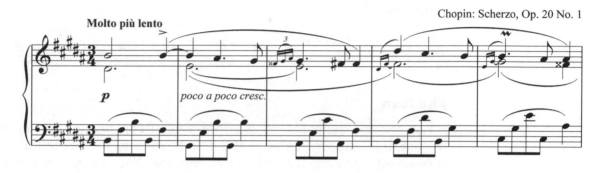

Played as:

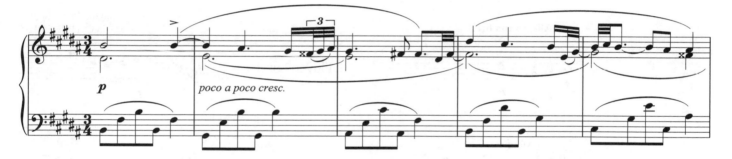

The appoggiatura

In the previous chapter we learnt that the appoggiatura is a non-chord note that occurs on the beat. Before about 1800 it was often written as an ornament (a small note, but without a stroke through its tail) in order to make the harmony note that follows it clearer. Again, it may be joined to the main note with a slur.

An appoggiatura usually takes half the value of the main note, or two-thirds if the main note is dotted. An appoggiatura can be written as a small crotchet, quaver or other note length to suggest its time value, but this is not always a reliable guide and performers use their discretion to determine exactly how long it should be.

Handel: 'I Know That my Redeemer Liveth' from *Messiah*

Could be performed as:

The mordent

A mordent consists of three notes and is a way of writing an auxiliary note as an ornament. An upper mordent (✳) is played by sounding the written note, the note above (the upper auxiliary) and then the written note again. A lower mordent (✳) is played by sounding the written note, the note below (the lower auxiliary) and then the written note again. Mordents are normally played as fast as possible. The auxiliary note is usually the one above or below, taking note of the sharps or flats in the key signature, unless an accidental is attached to the mordent sign to show how the auxiliary note should be altered:

Jacquet de la Guerre: 'Rondeau' from *Pièces de clavecin*

Played as:

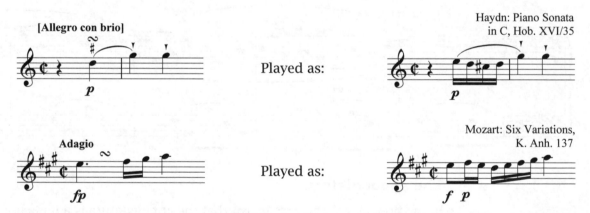

The turn

A turn (∾) is usually played as a four-note ornament, comprising the note above the written note, the written note, the note below and the written note again. The order is reversed when playing an inverted turn (⌇). The auxiliary notes are normally those above and below the main note, observing the key signature, unless accidentals above or below the symbol indicate otherwise:

[Allegro con brio]

Haydn: Piano Sonata in C, Hob. XVI/35

Played as:

p

Adagio

Mozart: Six Variations, K. Anh. 137

Played as:

fp

When a turn is placed over a note, as in the first example above, each of its four notes are normally a quarter of the length of the original note, especially at a fast tempo. When it is written *between* notes, as in the second example, the first note is shortened to make room for the ornament that follows. In all cases, the precise length of each note in a turn is usually decided by the performer to best suit the style and context of the music.

The trill

A trill is a rapid alternation of the written note with the one above, lasting for the duration of the written note. It is shown by writing *tr* above the note concerned, sometimes followed by a wavy line to show its duration. Until the early 19th century, trills were normally played starting on the note above the written note, but later it became common practice to start on the written note. Normally the upper note is one step above the main note (taking account of any sharps or flats in the key signature), unless an accidental is added to show how it should be altered. Trills are often combined with appoggiaturas, and are sometimes concluded with a turn:

Mozart: Flute Concerto in G, K. 313

[Allegro maestoso]

Played as:

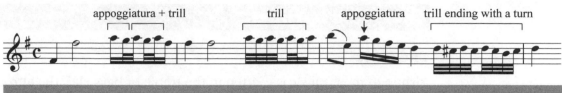

appoggiatura + trill   trill   appoggiatura   trill ending with a turn

Exercise 2

1. In which of the following bars should the notes sound (a) most detached, and (b) least detached?

2. How should you play a note that is marked *sfz*?

3. Explain the difference between > and ⌐ when written above a note.

4. Explain (a) the meaning of the symbol in bar 2 of the following, and (b) the meaning of *l.v.* in bar 4.

Cymbals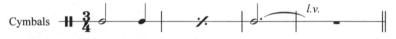

5. How should a violinist play the following?

con sord.

6. Which of the following double-stopped chords for cello is impossible, and why?

7. How should a pianist play a melody that is marked *coll' 8va*?

8. Rewrite the following passage using ornament signs in place of the bracketed notes.

Mozart: Clarinet Concerto, K. 622

[Adagio]

9. Explain the difference in interpretation between (a) and (b) below.

(a)   (b)

Bassoon   Timpani

5. Score reading

Clefs and barlines

The C clef

Although most music is written in the treble or bass clef, the alto C clef is used for the main part of the viola's range (changing to the treble clef for the higher notes). The central point of the alto C clef indicates middle C, which is on the middle line of the stave. When reading the alto clef (as it is usually called), remember that the C below middle C hangs below a single leger line beneath the stave, while the C an octave above middle C sits above a single leger line over the stave:

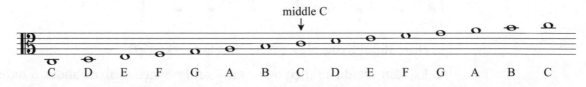

The tenor C clef has the same shape, but it is placed on the fourth line of the stave, and is used for high passages in cello, bassoon and trombone music:

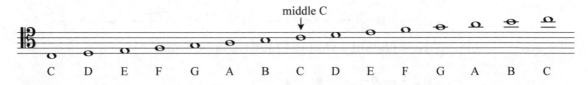

The flats or sharps in a key signature have to be written on the correct lines or spaces for the C clef, but they follow the same order that we learned for treble and bass clefs. In the case of sharps, that is <u>F</u>ather <u>C</u>harles <u>G</u>oes <u>D</u>own <u>A</u>nd <u>E</u>nds <u>B</u>attle:

In the case of flats, it is <u>B</u>attle <u>E</u>nds <u>A</u>nd <u>D</u>own <u>G</u>oes <u>C</u>harles's <u>F</u>ather:

Exercise 1

1. Rewrite the following viola part in the bass clef. Remember to include the key signature and check that you start on the right note by working out its pitch in relation to middle C (the note at the start of bar 2).

Berlioz: *Harold in Italy*

2. Rewrite the following tune in the tenor C clef. Remember to include the key signature and check that you start on the right note, one step below middle C. Notice that the tune should end on the same note.

Trad. Irish: *Lili Bulero*

The vocal tenor clef

We have already seen that stave notation for the guitar is written in the treble clef, but that it sounds an octave lower. Music for the tenor voice is treated similarly, and is usually written in the vocal tenor clef – a treble clef with the figure *8* attached to its tail as a reminder that it sounds an octave lower. So, the singer would read this:

Machaut: Rondo

and sing at this pitch:

Changing clef, key signature or time signature in a piece

Some instruments only ever use one clef – for example, music for the flute is always written in the treble clef. In other cases, it can make sense to change clef in order to avoid using too many leger lines. Here is a cello part written in the bass clef:

Saint-Saëns: 'The Swan' from *Carnival of the Animals*

This would be much easier to read if we start in the tenor clef and then move into the treble clef:

A change of clef is printed at the end of a bar where possible, using a small ('cue size') clef.

If the key signature needs to change during the course of a piece, write a double barline and then the new key signature. If the new key doesn't have a key signature, the accidentals of the old key signature are written as naturals straight after the double barline, as shown below – subsequent staves should be written without a key signature:

A change in time signature in the course of a piece is written after a single barline. If a new clef, key signature or time signature occurs at the start of a stave, the relevant symbols are also printed at the end of the previous stave to act as a warning:

Puccini: *La bohème* (Act 1)

Notice that the cue-sized clef comes before the barline, the key signature comes after, but before the time signature (as happens at the start of a piece) and there is no barline at the end of the stave, because one has already appeared after the clef change.

Double barlines

The type of double barline shown above, consisting of two thin lines, is used before a change of key signature and also at the ends of important sections within the music, such as between a verse and a chorus.

At the end of a movement or piece, we use a double barline consisting of a thin line followed by a thick line. This is also used, preceded by two dots, to show that a section should be repeated. If the repeat is not from the beginning, the start of the repeated section is shown by a mirror image of the same sign. Notice that the repeat dots go inside the double barlines:

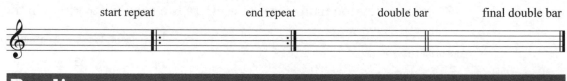

Reading a score

A score contains all the information needed to create a performance. Depending on the work, it may contain anything from a short piece for a single instrument to all the music needed for a substantial composition designed for a large orchestra and choir.

Layout

The example below shows how the start of a score should be laid out.

Suite 1

1. Prelude

J. S. Bach
(1685–1750)
BWV 1007

The title of the complete work is given at the top, with the number and name of the movement shown as a subtitle. The composer's name is written above the top stave on the right-hand side. Sometimes the composer's dates are given, along with an opus number (a work number) if there is one. The works of a number of composers have been catalogued by scholars and given reference numbers – here, BWV 1007 is the number of this suite in the standard catalogue of Bach's music. In a song, the name of the lyricist would also usually be included.

The name of the instrument is written at the start of the first stave, along with a tempo marking printed above the time signature. The tempo may be shown by a metronome marking. In this piece, the suggested speed is printed in square brackets to show that it has been added by a modern editor because, like much early music, there was no tempo marking in the original. Bar numbers are written at the start of each new stave, or may be printed every five or ten bars.

A clef and key signature (if there is one) must appear at the start of every stave in the music, but the time signature is given only at the beginning of the piece (immediately before the first note) and at any places where it changes.

A score for a single unaccompanied instrument

 The example on the previous page shows the opening of a piece for unaccompanied cello and so requires only a single stave throughout. Notice that there is no barline at the left end of a single-line stave. However, in music for an instrument that requires two staves (such as a piano or harp), the staves must be linked at their left ends to form a 'system' (that is, a group of staves intended to be performed simultaneously), using a barline and a curly brace, as shown here.

A score for one instrument and accompaniment

The score below contains three staves in each system, linked by a barline at the left end. In addition a brace joins each pair of piano staves. In an accompanied solo, the solo line is always written above the piano part. The full name of the solo instrument is written before its first stave. This can be omitted or abbreviated after the start. There is no necessity to label the piano stave, because two staves joined by a brace are always assumed to be for keyboard unless otherwise indicated.

The abbreviation 'trad.' indicates that this is a traditional melody, while 'arr.' means that it is an arrangement.

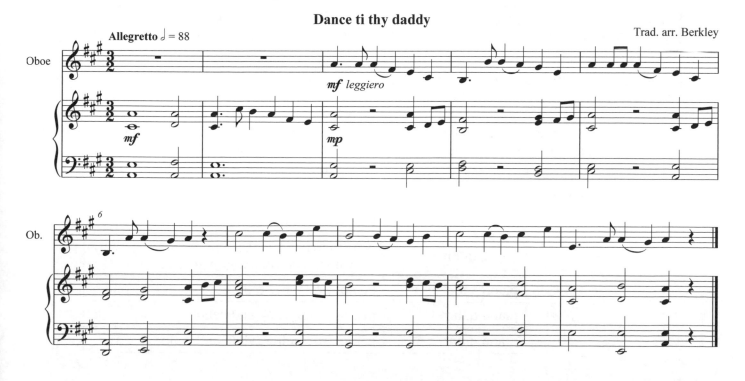

Dance ti thy daddy

Instrumental parts

In performance, the pianist will read from a score like the one above, showing the soloist's part as well as the accompaniment. However, the soloist will normally read from a part showing only the solo line. This helps to avoid or minimise awkward page turns in the middle of longer pieces. The solo part for this piece, which has been extracted from the score above, looks like this:

Dance ti thy daddy

A part for an individual instrument contains all the universal text (or system text) from the complete score – that is, items that apply to all the parts, such as title, composer and tempo. It also contains stave text, which is information that applies to only that part, such as marks of expression and other instructions for the performer concerned.

If there are several bars of continuous rests in a part, they may be written as a multiple rest to save space – here, the long rest at the start, with a figure 2 above it, tells the oboist to remain silent during the two bars of piano introduction. In the case of longer rests, the solo part may also include an outline of the accompaniment, printed as a 'cue' in smaller type above the rests to act as a reference point.

A score for three instruments

The example below is the start of a movement for string trio. The highest-sounding instrument is written on the top stave and the lowest on the bottom stave. The staves in each system are linked by a straight bracket at the left end. Notice that when a piece begins with an anacrusis, bar numbering starts from the first *complete* bar:

III. Scherzo

The members of a chamber ensemble like this would each play from their own part and may only refer to the complete score, if there is one, in rehearsals.

A string trio is one of a number of standard ensembles used in chamber music. Others include:

string quartet	two violins, viola and cello
string quintet	two violins, two violas and cello; or two violins, viola and two cellos
piano trio	piano, violin and cello
piano quartet	piano, violin, viola and cello
piano quintet	piano, two violins, viola and cello

wind trio	flute, oboe (or clarinet) and bassoon
wind quartet	flute, oboe, clarinet and bassoon
wind quintet	flute, oboe, clarinet, horn and bassoon
brass quartet	two trumpets, trombone and tuba
brass quintet	two trumpets, horn, trombone and tuba

Vocal scores and short scores

The piece below is for four-part choir accompanied by organ. The vocal parts for soprano, alto, tenor and bass (or SATB) are laid out in descending order of pitch. Brackets show that tempo and dynamics have been added by an editor, and the right-hand of the organ part is printed in small notes to indicate that this has also been provided by a modern editor.

Exsultate Justi

Lodovico Viadana

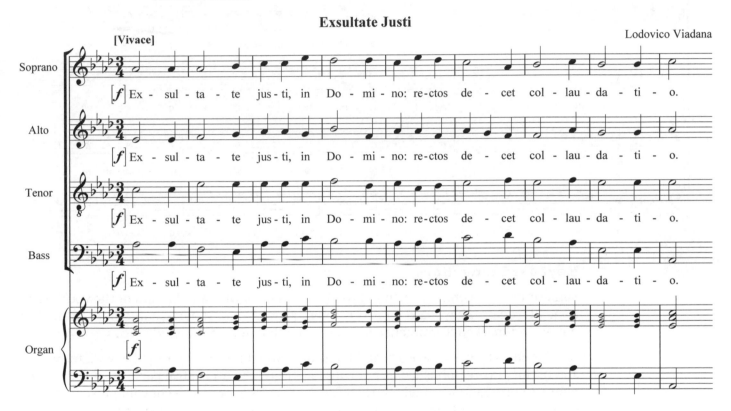

This layout, in which each vocal part has its own stave, is called a **vocal score**. Notice that each voice part has its own dynamic and lyrics, with the syllables in multiple-syllable words separated by hyphens. Choral singers usually read from vocal scores, and not from separate vocal parts.

Vocal music can also be written in **short score**, in which adjacent voice parts share a stave, usually soprano and alto on a treble stave and tenor and bass on a bass stave. The tenor part is written in the bass clef, and so looks different to the way it would in a vocal score, but the sounding pitches remain the same. In a short score, the upper part on each stave is written entirely with note stems pointing up, and the lower part with stems pointing down. Here is the opening of the vocal parts of *Exsultate Justi* written in short score:

A short score works best when the vocal parts are mainly in the same rhythm. When the musical texture is more complex, as in the next example, then it can look confusing:

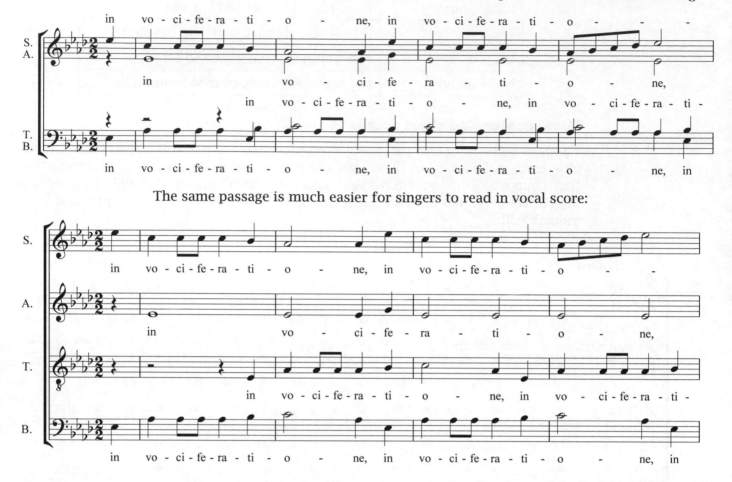

The same passage is much easier for singers to read in vocal score:

Keyboard reductions

Sometimes unaccompanied choral works are printed with a reduction of the vocal parts to be played on a keyboard. This is printed below the vocal parts, sometimes in smaller notes, and marked 'for practise only'. A reduction does not include lyrics.

A different type of keyboard reduction is used when the vocal parts of a work for voices and orchestra are published as a vocal score. Here, the orchestral parts are arranged for piano, to provide a less bulky format for the singers as well as a convenient score to use in rehearsals, where only a pianist often has to provide the accompaniment.

Lead sheets

Because lead sheets give comparatively little detail about the music, you should check with your teacher if this format is suitable for a composition before using it for an exam submission.

In jazz and pop music, musicians often perform from a lead sheet, which contains just the melody (sometimes with lyrics, if it is a song) and chord symbols (sometimes with guitar grids). Lead sheets are often written with four bars in each line, and arranged so that the music fits onto one page for convenient reading:

Performers derive their own parts from this type of score in different ways. A soloist will take the melody, often adapting it to suit the style of performance – in the case of a song, one or more sections might be played by an instrumentalist to give the singer a rest. Those playing chords, such as a pianist or rhythm guitarist, will improvise an accompaniment based on the chord symbols. The bass player will use the chords as a foundation for the bass part, typically playing chord notes on the beat and adding non-chord notes off the beat. The drummer, too, may use the structure of the song shown in the lead sheet as a template for devising a suitable drum part.

Jazz and pop performers use the lead sheet as a blueprint for their performances, and each artist will create a different piece by modifying the mood and style of the music, although keeping the key elements of melody, structure and chords similar. Listen to *Autumn Leaves* sung by Eva Cassidy accompanied by acoustic guitar, and by Frank Sinatra or Nat 'King' Cole who are accompanied by orchestra. Listen also to instrumental versions of this piece by the trumpeter Miles Davies (with bass, drums and rhythm guitar), and the pianists Bill Evans or Keith Jarrett (with drums and string bass).

Pop and jazz arrangements

Lead sheets are mainly used by small groups – they don't work well for larger bands, where simultaneous improvisation is likely to result in musically confused textures. Larger bands usually require written-out arrangements, although these often include some lightly-scored sections in which a soloist can improvise from a chord pattern. Performers play from parts extracted from a full score like the one below. Notice that both alto saxophones share a stave, as do the trumpets (with rests adjusted vertically to make their individual lines clear). The two saxophone staves are bracketed together because they are for similar types of instrument.

Ma
(He's Making Eyes At Me)

Con Conrad (1891–1938)

This type of score clearly contains much more detail than a simple lead sheet. Can you work out who is playing what? The melody (marked 'solo') is played by the first trumpet and **doubled** (that is, duplicated) an octave lower by the tenor saxophone. The rest of the horn section (the term used in jazz for wind and brass instruments) plays a syncopated motif during the long notes of the tune, while the rhythm section (guitar, drums and bass in this arrangement) plays a supportive accompaniment.

In a big band, the horn section is likely to be considerably larger than the one in the arrangement above (and will usually include trombones), the rhythm section could include a pianist and perhaps some Latin-American percussion instruments, and there could also be a solo vocalist and backing singers.

Orchestral scores

In a score for a large orchestra, the parts are laid out with the woodwind instruments (from highest to lowest) at the top of the system. The horns come next, because horns and woodwind often play together. Then comes the rest of the brass, from highest to lowest (trumpets, trombones and tuba). Percussion parts are written below the brass, and finally comes the strings, again in order from highest to lowest – first violins, second violins, violas, cellos and double basses. If there are vocal, harp or keyboard parts, they are written between the percussion and the strings. If there is a part for a soloist (as in a concerto), it will usually be placed above the first-violin part.

To make it easier to follow such a large system, brackets on the left group together the staves for each orchestral family (strings, woodwind and so on). There may also be curly braces to link staves for similar instruments, such as the first and second violins, or the staves for the trombones.

The conductor generally uses a full score printed in a large format, which is easy to see from a distance in performance. Many well-known pieces are also published in smaller versions (called study scores, pocket scores or miniature scores) for study purposes.

Pairs of wind parts are usually printed on the same stave: in bars 1 and 2 of the horn and trumpet parts, player 1 takes the top notes and player 2 takes the lower notes. The instruction 'a 2' in wind and brass parts means both musicians should play the same notes. Simultaneous notes in a string part, as in the violin parts of bars 4–7 below, are assumed to be double stops unless the part is marked *div.* (*divisi*), in which case the notes are divided between players. After such a passage, the instruction *unis.* (*unisono*) indicates that the players should revert to all playing the same notes in unison. Any part marked 'solo' or '1.' should be performed by only one musician.

Symphony in C major, K.V. 425

Minuet

W.A.Mozart (1756–1791)

The score above is written for a relatively small orchestra. A large symphony orchestra may contain 80–100 musicians, typically with:

➤ A woodwind section of flutes and piccolo, oboes and cor anglais, clarinets and bass clarinet, bassoons and double bassoon

➤ A brass section of horns, trumpets, trombones and tuba

➤ A percussion section that includes timpani plus several musicians who typically play snare drum, bass drum, cymbals, triangle, tambourine, gong, xylophone, tubular bells and glockenspiel, and who may be called upon to play Latin-American and other types of percussion

➤ Often a harp (and there may be keyboard instruments such as a celesta or piano)

➤ A large string section of first and second violins, violas, cellos and double basses, often forming around 60% of the orchestra as a whole.

In an orchestral score, there are staves for every part at the start of the music with instrument names given in full. After this, only the staves being played are printed in subsequent systems, with abbreviated instrument names, in order to save paper and reduce the number of page turns. Where two or more systems are printed on a page they are separated by two diagonal lines called a system separator, as can be seen in the next example.

Following a large score is not easy at first, especially when the number of staves per system changes. It is often best to concentrate on the first-violin part, which usually contains much of the main melodic material, allowing the eye to take in other staves when the focus of interest moves to a different part.

Band scores

Scores for a large band are set out in a similar way to orchestral scores, although there won't be any string parts.

A typical **brass band** includes cornets, flugel horns, tenor horns, baritone horns (usually called baritones), trombones, euphonium, tuba or bass horn, timpani and percussion.

A **concert band** (or wind band) can include almost all wind, brass and percussion instruments. Here is the opening of an arrangement of Purcell's *Evening Hymn* for concert band. Notice the use of a system separator between the first (complete) system and the second (eight-stave) system:

Evening Hymn

Henry Purcell (1659–1695)
arr. Berkley

Transposing instruments

Here is the opening of the trumpet part in the arrangement of Purcell's *Evening Hymn* that we saw on the previous page:

Here is the same part after it has been extracted from the score, ready for the players to use:

The second example is one tone higher than the first, being written in G major instead of F major. This is because the trumpet, like the clarinet, saxophone and horn, is a transposing instrument. Non-transposing instruments, like the flute, oboe, violin and piano, sound C if C is played. On a transposing instrument, playing C will cause a note of a different pitch to sound – in most cases, a lower pitch.

The difference in pitch can usually be worked out from the instrument's full name, which includes the note that sounds when C is played. So, when C is played on a trumpet in B♭, it will sound as B♭ one tone lower. From this we can deduce that every note will sound one tone lower than written on a trumpet in B♭.

Instruments in B♭

Like the trumpet in B♭, the clarinet in B♭ sounds notes that are a tone lower than written. The tenor saxophone is also a B♭ instrument, but being a large treble-clef instrument, its notes sound an octave plus a tone (i.e. a major 9th) lower than written. If a B♭ clarinet plays this melody:

it will sound one tone lower, like this:

So, we can see that parts for clarinets in B♭ and trumpets in B♭ have to be written a tone higher than they are intended to sound, in order to come out at the right pitch. Similarly, music for the tenor saxophone in B♭ has to be written an octave and a tone higher than it is to sound.

The clarinet in A

Experienced clarinettists use two instruments, one in B♭ and one in A. When the A clarinet plays a C, it sounds as A, a minor 3rd lower. Parts for the clarinet in A therefore have to be written a minor 3rd higher than they are to sound:

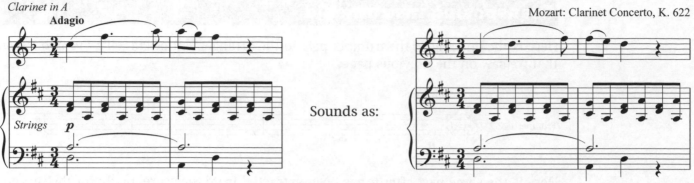

Notice that music for non-transposing instruments (such as the strings in the example above) is always written at sounding pitch – it is only parts for transposing instruments that need to be written at a different pitch.

E♭ instruments

The alto saxophone is in E♭. When it plays a C, the note sounds as E♭, a major 6th lower. The baritone saxophone is also in E♭, but being a very large treble-clef instrument it sounds an octave plus a major 6th lower than written.

A rather rarer instrument is the small clarinet in E♭. It too sounds E♭ when C is played, but it is one of the few cases in which the sounding pitch is higher than the written pitch. So parts for the clarinet in E♭ sound a minor 3rd *higher* than written.

F instruments

Modern horns are normally in F: when C is played, the note sounds as F, a perfect 5th lower, so horn parts have to be written a perfect 5th higher than they sound. In older music horn parts are found in a variety of keys, but the same principle applies: an instrument 'in X' sounds the pitch X when C is played.

The cor anglais is also an instrument in F, but it's one of the few where the interval of transposition doesn't appear in the instrument's full name. Nevertheless, it is easy to remember if you think of it as an English *horn*, because this will remind you that, like the modern orchestral horn, it is in F.

Instruments which transpose at the octave

Very high instruments, such as the piccolo and descant recorder, sound an octave higher than written:

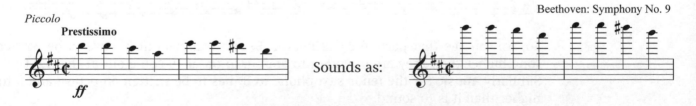

As you can see, writing the music an octave lower than it sounds saves having to use a confusing number of leger lines.

Similarly, very low instruments such as the double bass, double bassoon and bass guitar sound an octave lower than written. As we noted earlier, the guitar also sounds an octave lower than written, allowing its part to be written entirely in the treble clef.

Common transposing instruments

Instrument	If reading a C the note sounds	Write the part
Guitar	C an octave lower	An octave higher, using the vocal tenor clef
Piccolo and descant recorder	C an octave higher	An octave lower
Cor Anglais	F a perfect 5th lower	A perfect 5th higher
Clarinet in B♭ and soprano sax in B♭	B♭ a tone lower	A tone higher
Clarinet in A	A a minor 3rd lower	A minor 3rd higher
Clarinet in E♭	E♭ a minor 3rd higher	A minor 3rd lower
Bass Clarinet in B♭	B♭ a major 9th lower	A major 9th higher in the treble clef
Alto Saxophone in E♭	E♭ a major 6th lower	A major 6th higher
Tenor Saxophone in B♭	B♭ a major 9th lower	A major 9th higher
Baritone saxophone in E♭	E♭ an octave plus a major 6th lower	An octave plus a major 6th higher in the treble clef
Trumpet in B♭	B♭ a tone lower	A tone higher
Glockenspiel	C two octaves higher	Two octaves lower
Xylophone	C one octave higher	One octave lower
Celesta	C one octave higher	One octave lower

Non-transposing instruments (sometimes called instruments 'in C') include the violin, viola, cello, flute, oboe, bassoon, timpani, harp and piano. These instruments all sound at written pitch.

Music for the tuba is normally written in the bass clef at sounding pitch. However, in the brass-band tradition it is often taught as a treble-clef instrument to match the fingering of other brass instruments. When written in the treble clef, the B♭ tuba is treated as a transposing instrument that sounds two octaves plus a tone lower than written. Similarly, a part for the E♭ tuba, when written in the treble clef, sounds an octave plus a major 6th lower than written (like a baritone saxophone). In brass-band music, the tenor trombone is also treated as a treble-clef transposing instrument (sounding a major 9th lower than written, like the tenor saxophone).

Exercise 2

Using appropriate key signatures, rewrite the following melody to be played on (i) cor anglais, (ii) clarinet in A, (iii) alto saxophone and (iv) trumpet in B♭, so that in each case the notes will sound at the same pitch as the printed melody.

(i)

(ii)

(iii)

(iv)

Transposition in scores

The arrangement of Purcell's *Evening Hymn* on page 74 is printed with all parts written at sounding pitch. This is known as a score at concert pitch, and is usually a perfectly acceptable way in which to submit compositions for exam purposes. You may need to use non-standard clefs when there is no transposition – for example, a part for baritone saxophone will almost certainly need to be written in the bass clef, and instruments such as the tenor saxophone and horn may need to change between treble and bass clefs during the course of the piece. If you are performing the piece, you will of course need to transpose the parts, but this can be handled automatically if you use computer software to notate your work.

Normally, though, parts for transposing instruments in published scores are printed in the key that the performer reads from, so a conductor can see the pitches that the player sees when referring to a particular passage.

6. Exercises

This chapter contains exercises that bring together many of the points explained earlier in the book. In each case, read through the music in the score (and play it, if possible) and then answer the questions that follow. References such as bar 3² mean bar 3, beat 2.

Exercise 1

1. Name the type of chord used at *(a)*.

2. What enharmonic equivalent could be used for the first note (A♯) of the melody?

3. Name the type of chord used at *(b)*. (Tip: thinking of an enharmonic equivalent to A♯ should help you identify this chord).

4. What type of non-chord note is used at *(c)*?

5. What type of non-chord notes are used at *(d)*?

6. This passage begins in G major. In which key does it end? How is this new key related to G major?

7. The chord in bar 6 is a pivot chord. Give its Roman numeral in terms of both the key that is being left (G major) and the new key that is being approached. Remember that the accidentals in this bar are purely chromatic.

8. What type of chord is heard at the start of bar 7 (marked *(e)*)?

9. How should the notes marked with a slurred staccato in bars 1 and 3 be played?

10. What is the meaning of the horizontal dashes over the notes in bar 7?

11. Name the rhythmic feature that occurs in every complete bar of the melody.

12. Write out the upper notes of the melody in bars 5 and 6 for clarinet in A, so that they would sound at the same pitch. Remember to add the new key signature.

Exercise 2

Corelli: Concerto Grosso, Op. 6 No. 1

1. The parts in this score are for three soloists (two violinists and a cellist) and a string orchestra. Label the first system with the names of the instruments.

2. When performing this style of music, the orchestral cello part is usually also played by a double bass. What difference in pitch will this make to the part?

3. This excerpt is from a movement that begins and ends in D major. Name the key of the music in the following bars, and state how each key is related to D major (e.g. 'subdominant'). There are two minim beats per bar.

   (a) 0^2–2^1 (b) 2^2–4^1 (c) 4^2–6^1 (d) 6^2–12^1

4. How do the solo violin parts relate to the orchestral violin parts from the beginning of the extract until the start of bar 6?

5. Complete this sentence with the correct technical term:

   In the final bars, the solo parts are all .... by the orchestra.

6. What sign might you pencil into the score if you wanted to remind the players to start with an up bow after the rest in bar 10?

7. At the start of the second minim beat in bar 11, the second violins sustain F♯ against G♯ played by the first violins. What type of non-chord note is the F♯?

8. Rewrite the viola part from bar 8 to the end in the treble clef so that it sounds at the same pitch:

Exercise 3

1. This score is written at concert pitch. What does this mean?

2. Which two of the following terms best describe the trumpet melody? Underline two answers.

   chromatic   diatonic   enharmonic   hexatonic   pentatonic

3. (a) On what instrument should the x-headed notes in bar 1 of the drum part be played?

   (b) What does the symbol ⁒ in bar 2 of the drum part mean?

   (c) What does *l.v.* in the last bar of the drum part mean?

4. Name the cadence at the end of the first phrase (bars 3–4).

5. Name the chord progression in bars 6–8.

6. Identify the type of chord used on each of the beats marked *(a)*, *(b)* and *(c)* in bars 14–15 (tip: all of the notes of each chord appear in the piano part).

7. (a) How does the pianist decorate the final tonic chord?

   (b) Where else in the extract is this same type of non-chord note used?

8. What is the meaning of 'straight 8s' in bar 8?

9. Write out the two top staves of bars 1–2 for trumpet in B♭ and alto saxophone in E♭ as the players would need to read them in order to sound at the pitches printed in the score. Remember to add the correct key signature and time signature to each part.

Trumpet in B♭

Alto sax. in E♭

Exercise 4

Andantino quasi allegretto (♩ = 52)

Rimsky-Korsakov: *Scheherazade*

1. What is the correct time signature for this music?

2. What is the purpose of the letter G at the start of the score?

3. The staves in this excerpt are labelled in Italian (using abbreviations in many cases). Fill in the table below with the full English name of each instrument. Remember to include the key of any transposing instruments.

	Stave label	English name in full
Woodwind	Picc.	
	Fl.	
	Ob.	
	C.i.	
	Cl.	
	Fg.	
Brass	Cor.	
	Trb.	
	Trbn.	
	Tb.	
Percussion	Timp.	
	Triangolo	
	Tamburino	
	Tamburo piccolo	
	Piatti	
Other	Arpa	
Strings	Vln. I	
	Vln. II	
	Vla.	
	Vc.	
	Cb.	

4. What do the following instructions and symbols mean?

(a) *pizz.* (strings, bar 1)

(b)  ♩ (tamburo piccolo, bar 1)

(c)  { (arpa, bar 1)

(d) 1. (trb., bar 1)

(e) > (picc., bar 1)

(f) a 2 (cor., bar 7)

5. Here is a keyboard reduction of this extract:

(a) Which instruments play this melody?

(b) Which instruments play the bass part printed above?

(c) Complete the right-hand part of this keyboard reduction, adding appropriate chords from the orchestral score. Remember to take account of transposing instruments and use the same rhythm as the bass line.

6. How are the viola and cello parts related in bars 5–8? Underline one answer.

       in octaves   in parallel 4ths   in unison

7. Comment on the rhythm of the tambourine part in bars 1–6.

8. Underline the name of the instrument that plays in unison with the first horn in bars 1–2 and 5–6 (remember to take account of transposition):

       cor anglais   first trombone   oboe

9. Precisely what type of non-chord note is the C♯ that occurs in the melody of bars 1–4?

Exercise 5

[au Mouvement]

Debussy: 'Reflets dans l'eau' from *Images*

treble stave only

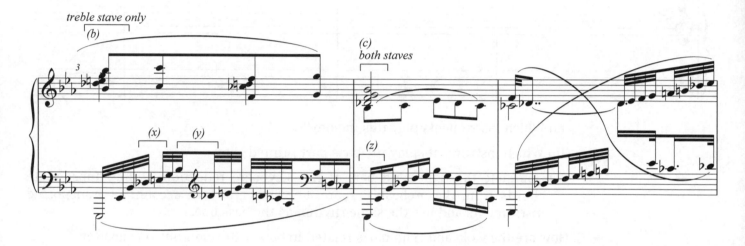

1. This piano piece uses demisemiquaver, semiquaver and quaver triplets, but the triplet numbers have been left out at the start of the extract above. Add the figure 3 to the beams (or, if necessary, add triplet brackets) where required in bars 1–3 only.

2. Using chord labels (not Roman numerals), identify the chords marked *(a)*, *(b)* and *(c)*.

3. Name the harmonic device used in bars 1–4[1].

4. Which of the following scales occurs in bar 5? Underline your answer.

   C melodic minor   chromatic   mixolydian   whole tone

5. In which two other bars do all the notes come from this same scale?

6. Explain what is meant by the crossing phrase marks in bar 5, 7 and 8.

7. What is meant by the symbol *8va* followed by a dashed bracket in bar 7?

8. Identify the melodic intervals marked *(x)*, *(y)* and *(z)*.

9. At the start of this movement (before the printed extract begins), the composer wrote 'Tempo rubato'. How should the pianist interpret this instruction?

Exercise 6

Lieblich (Gracefully)

Schubert: *Heidenröslein*, D. 257

Voice

Sah ein Knab ein Rös - lein stehn, Rös - lein auf der Hei - den, war so jung und

mor - gen - schön, lief er schnell, es nah zu sehn, sah's mit vie - len

Cadence x

Freu - den. nachgebend (*rall.*) Rös - lein, Rös - lein, Rös - lein rot, wie oben (*a tempo*) Rös - lein auf der Hei - den.

Cadence y

1. Identify the four melodic intervals marked *(a)*, *(b)*, *(c)* and *(d)*.

2. In the melody of bars 1–4, identify one example of a passing note, and one example of an accented passing note.

3. Label the chords in bars 1–4 using Roman numerals. (Tip: Read the notes of the piano part first and look for non-chord notes in the melody.)

4. Rewrite the melody of bars 7–10, beaming the notes correctly and adding slurs to show how the syllables fit the tune (there is no need to include the words):

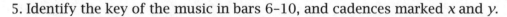

5. Identify the key of the music in bars 6–10, and cadences marked *x* and *y*.

6. What name is given to cadences that end on a weak beat, such as these?

7. State the bar numbers in which each of the following chords occur:

   (a) IIb in D major (Em/G)   (b) Ic in G major (G/D)

8. Explain precisely how the tempo changes in bars 11–12.

Glossary

Acciaccatura. A very short ornamental note (♪) played just before a principal melodic note. From the Italian *acciaccare*, 'to crush'.

Accidental. A symbol that changes the pitch of a note. A sharp (♯) written before a note raises its pitch by a semitone, while a flat (♭) lowers its pitch by a semitone. A natural (♮) cancels any earlier sharps or flats, including those in the key signature.

Anacrusis. An upbeat. An unaccented note or group of notes that come before the first strong beat of a phrase. At the start of a piece an anacrusis forms an incomplete bar.

Anticipation (note of anticipation). A note played immediately before the chord to which it belongs, so creating a dissonance with the current chord. The anticipated note is often the tonic in a perfect cadence.

Appoggiatura. A note (sometimes written as an ornament) that falls on the beat as a dissonance and then resolves by step onto the main note. From the Italian *appoggiare*, 'to lean'.

Articulation. The manner in which a series of notes are played with regards to their separation or connection – for example, staccato (separated) or legato (connected).

Augmentation. Proportionally lengthening the note values of a passage of music. For example, a melody in quavers is augmented if it then appears in crotchets.

Augmented interval. An interval that is one semitone wider than a major or perfect interval. An augmented 5th (e.g. G♭–D) is one semitone wider than a perfect 5th (G–D); an augmented 3rd (e.g. F–A♯) is one semitone wider than a major 3rd (F–A).

Auxiliary note. A non-chord note that occurs between, and is a step away from, two harmony notes of the same pitch.

Beat. The beat in a piece of music is a regular pulse that we can clap along to. The number of beats in each bar is indicated by the time signature: for example, a time signature of ⁴⁄₄ tells us that there are four crotchet beats in each bar.

Cadence. A type of musical punctuation formed by the last two chords of a phrase. *See* **Imperfect cadence**, **Interrupted cadence**, **Perfect cadence** and **Plagal cadence**.

Cadential ⁶⁄₄. The second inversion of the tonic chord used immediately before a dominant chord at a cadence. It consists of the dominant note in the bass, plus notes that are a 6th and a 4th above the dominant.

Chromatic note. A note that does not belong to the scale of the key that the music is currently in. For example, B♮ and D♯ are chromatic notes in the key of F major. Opposite of **Diatonic note**.

Circle of 5ths. (1) A diagram showing the relationship between different keys, in which the 12 major keys are arranged in a circle; going clockwise around the circle each successive key is a fifth higher, while going anticlockwise each key is a fifth lower. (2) A chord progression in which the root of each chord is a 5th lower (or a 4th higher) than the previous one.

Compound time. *See* **Simple and compound time**.

Diatonic note. A note that belongs to the scale of the key that the music is currently in. For example, B♭ and D are diatonic notes in the key of F major. Opposite of **Chromatic note**.

Diminution. Proportionally shortening the note values of a passage of music. For example, a melody in minims is diminished if it then appears in crotchets.

Diminished interval. An interval that is one semitone narrower than a minor or perfect interval. A diminished 4th (e.g. G♯–C) is one semitone narrower than a perfect 4th (G–C); a diminished 6th (e.g. B–G♭) is one semitone narrower than a minor 6th (B–G).

Dissonance. Created by sounds that are considered unstable, requiring resolution, and harsh or challenging to listen to.

Dominant. The fifth degree of a major or minor scale.

Dominant 7th chord. A dominant chord with a minor 7th added above the root, frequently used as the first chord of a perfect cadence (V⁷–I). For example, A–C♯–E–G is the dominant 7th chord of D major.

Enharmonic (enharmonic equivalents). The same pitch notated in two different ways. For example, A♯ and B♭.

Grace note. A short ornamental note printed in small type. The most common grace note is the **acciaccatura**.

Harmonic. On string instruments (including the harp and guitar) a very high and pure sound produced by placing the finger on a string very lightly before plucking or bowing.

Harmonic interval. The interval between two notes that are played or sung at the same time. *See also* **Melodic interval**.

Harmonic minor scale. *See* **Minor scale**.

Harmony note. A note that belongs to the chord being played. For example, in a chord of D major an F♯ is a harmony note, whereas a B is a non-harmony or **non-chord note**.

Hemiola. The articulation of two units of triple time (*strong–weak–weak, strong–weak–weak*) as three units of duple time (*strong–weak, strong–weak, strong–weak*).

Hexatonic scale. A scale made up of six notes. For example, a hexatonic scale on D might be D–E–F♯–G–A–B.

Imperfect cadence. A cadence consisting of any chord – usually I, ii or IV – followed by the dominant (V).

Improvisation. The process, most common in jazz, of spontaneously creating new music, often based on existing musical material (such as a chord pattern).

Interrupted cadence. A cadence consisting of the dominant chord (V) followed by any chord except I (most often VI).

Inversion. (1) In an inverted chord the lowest note is not the root. In a first-inversion chord the 3rd is the lowest note, and in a second inversion chord the 5th is the lowest note. For example, a tonic triad of F major in first inversion is A–C–F, and in second inversion is C–F–A. (2) In an inverted melody rising intervals become falling ones and vice versa, so the inverted melody looks like a mirror image of the original. (3) In an inverted interval the lowest note is transposed up an octave. For example, when the interval F–A (a major 3rd) is inverted, it becomes A–F (a minor 6th).

Leading note. The seventh degree of a major or minor scale.

Mediant. The third degree of a major or minor scale.

Melodic interval. The interval between two notes that are played or sung one after the other. *See also* **Harmonic interval**.

Melodic minor scale. *See* **Minor scale**.

Metronome marking. An indication of how fast to play a piece by specifying how many beats per minute there should be. For example, a metronome marking of ♩ = 60 means that there are 60 crotchet beats per minute, or one crotchet beat per second.

Minor scale (natural, harmonic, melodic). The natural minor scale uses the same notes as its **relative major**, but starts two scale steps lower. For example, a scale of A natural minor uses the same notes as C major but starts two steps lower, forming the pattern A–B–C–D–E–F–G–A. In the harmonic minor scale the seventh degree of the natural minor scale is raised by a semitone; for example, the scale of A harmonic minor is A–B–C–D–E–F–G♯–A. In a melodic minor scale, the sixth and seventh degrees of the natural minor are raised when going up, and returned to normal when going down; for example, the notes of the full A melodic minor scale are A–B–C–D–E–F♯–G♯–A–G♮–F♮–E–D–C–B–A.

Modes (aeolian, dorian, ionian, mixolydian). Seven-note scales that can be created using only the white notes of a piano keyboard. The dorian can be played beginning on D (i.e. D–E–F–G–A–B–C–D), the mixolydian on G, the aeolian on A and the ionian on C. These interval patterns can then be transposed to start on any other note: for example, dorian beginning on G (or 'G dorian') would be G–A–B♭–C–D–E–F–G.

Modulation. The process of changing key.

Mordent. A quickly played ornament which begins on the written note, moves up a step (upper mordent, ⤮) or down a step (lower mordent, ⤭) and then returns to the original note. The non-written note can be chromatically altered by an **accidental**, written just above the mordent symbol.

Natural minor scale. *See* **Minor scale**.

Non-chord note. A note that does not belong to the chord being played. For example, the note B heard against a chord of C major (C–E–G) would be a non-harmony note. *See also* **Harmony note**.

Passing note. A non-harmony note placed between, and connecting, two different harmony notes usually a 3rd apart.

Pentatonic scale. A scale of five notes. A major pentatonic scale is formed from the first, second, third, fifth and sixth degrees of a major scale. A minor pentatonic scale is formed from the first, third, fourth, fifth and seventh degrees of a natural minor scale.

Perfect cadence. A **cadence** consisting of the dominant chord (V or V⁷) followed by the tonic (I).

Pivot chord. A chord that links two different keys in a **modulation** and whose notes are common to both of them. For example, a chord of A minor occurs in the keys of C major and G major, and so could be used as a pivot chord between the two.

Plagal cadence. A **cadence** consisting of the subdominant chord (IV) followed by the tonic (I).

Relative major/relative minor. Keys that have the same key signature but a different scale pattern. A relative minor is three semitones down the scale from its relative major: for example, C major and A minor, or F major and D minor.

Root. The note on which a chord is built and after which it takes its name. For example, the root of a chord of D minor is the note D.

Simple and compound time. In simple time the beat can be divided into two (for example a crotchet beat can be divided into two quavers). In compound time the beat can be divided into three (for example a dotted crotchet beat can be divided into three quavers). Thus $\frac{2}{2}$ and $\frac{3}{4}$ are simple time signatures, and $\frac{6}{4}$ and $\frac{9}{8}$ are compound time signatures.

Sounding pitch. The pitch that sounds when a note is played by a transposing instrument.

Subdominant. The fourth degree of a major or minor scale.

Supertonic. The second degree of a major of minor scale.

Suspension. A device in which a note that is sounded as part of a chord (the preparation) is then held or repeated over a change in harmony to create a dissonance (the suspension), before moving stepwise (normally downwards) to a note of the new chord (the resolution).

Tablature. A method of notation for plucked instruments such as the lute and guitar, in which the pitches of the notes are indicated by their fingering.

Texture. The relationship between the various simultaneous lines in a passage of music, dependent on such features as the number and function of the parts and the spacing between them.

Tonality. The use of major and minor keys in music and the ways in which these keys are related. Not all music is tonal – some is modal (based on one or more **modes**) and some makes use of non-western scales. Western pieces that use neither keys nor modes are described as atonal ('without tonality').

Tonic. The first degree of a major or minor scale.

Transposing instrument. An instrument in which the **sounding pitch** differs from the written pitch of the instrument's part. An instrument's **transposition** from C is often indicated in its name (although one notable exception is the cor anglais); for example, Horn in F (in which the sounding pitch is a perfect fifth below written pitch), Clarinet in B♭ (in which the sounding pitch is a whole tone below written pitch).

Transposition. The movement up or down in pitch of a whole passage or piece of music.

Triad. A chord of three notes: the root and notes a 3rd and 5th above it.

Trill. An ornament (**tr**) consisting of a rapid alternation of two adjacent pitches, usually for the duration of the ornamented note. The non-written note can be chromatically altered by an **accidental**, written just above the trill.

Turn. An ornament (∿) consisting of the note above the written note, the written note, the note below the written note, and the written note again. The non-written notes can be chromatically altered by **accidentals**, written above or below the sign.

Whole-tone scale. A scale in which the interval between every successive note is a whole tone.

Index